FEATURES

KNITTING

COOKERY

Printed and published in Great Britain by D. C. Thomson & Co., Ltd., Dundee, Glasgow, London and Manchester.

£2.35

The Day We

Complete Story
by LAEL J. LITTKE

Lost Max

Many a mother will recognise Max. He's the smallest, the youngest, the easiest to lose in a crowd of children — and the easiest to love.

WE probably wouldn't even have noticed that Max had fallen out of the pick-up van if Ralph hadn't seen him go. That's the way Max was.

He could sit right next to you for hours, sucking his thumb and sometimes humming a little to himself, and you wouldn't even know he was there, and when you finally noticed he wasn't, you wouldn't be able to remember just when he left.

He was Aunt Fiona's youngest, the last of eleven robust children. Aunt Fiona herself said she sometimes had a hard time remembering he was around, since in all his five years he had made hardly any more noise than the soft slurping as he sucked his thumb, and the occasional humming.

Aunt Fiona, Mum, three of our kids, and six of Aunt Fiona's were on our way to visit Aunt Blanche at Hill Farm when Max fell out.

It was crowded in the back of the pick-up van, what with nine of us kids trying to cling somewhere so we wouldn't bounce out.

Ralph said Max stood up, probably to shift his position, and just then the truck hit a bump in the road. Max went over the side without a sound.

"Max fell out," said Ralph in a hoarse, scared voice.

We didn't hear him over the roar of the engine, so Ralph began pointing frantically back down the road. There, beside a clump of weeds into which he had fallen, Max stood watching us retreat, a thumb still in his mouth.

"Mum!" screamed Una, banging to attract attention. "Mum, Max fell out!"

"Stop that banging!" bellowed Aunt Fiona.

My brother Oliver pounded on Mum's side. "Max fell out!" he yelled.

Mum called something, but we couldn't hear it above the engine's noise.

We all looked at one another, our eyes enormous. "Mum!" we wailed collectively. "Stop!"

Alas! Too often had we cried "wolf" in the past. Too often we had played tricks on Mum and Aunt Fiona. If they heard us at all they discounted our cries as just another prank.

What could we do? Leonard volunteered to crawl out of the truck on to the running board, but Aunt Fiona saw him in the mirror and in turning round to tell him to get back in, made the truck zig-zag across the road.

Through the window of the cab we could see Mum and Aunt Fiona talking together, so engrossed in their conversation that they probably wouldn't have noticed if all of us had fallen out.

They always discussed life when they were driving along like that. Any child lucky enough to ride up front could learn some pretty interesting things, since they were apt to forget you were there, especially if you sat still and pretended to be asleep.

I had an idea they were talking about how Jenny Calder had run off with a linoleum salesman three months ago, and had just come home; and how everyone told Sam he shouldn't take her back.

He said he was tired of feeding the chickens and getting his own meals, and Jenny was a good worker and a fine cook even though she did crave a little excitement now and then.

BY the time Aunt Fiona stopped the van in Aunt Blanche's yard we were all in a state of shock and just sat there trying to find our voices.

Aunt Blanche and several of her children came running out.

"My stars," she said, looking into the back of the van where we sat, "the kids are all car-sick. All pale and round eyed."

Aunt Fiona climbed down from the cab and looked at us. "What's the matter?" she asked.

"Max fell out," whispered Una.

"Max?" said Aunt Fiona.

"Fell out," whispered Ralph.

Mum got down from the running board where she was standing, and she and Aunt Fiona stirred through all of us children as if they expected to uncover Max somewhere in our midst.

"Max isn't here," Aunt Fiona said.

"He fell out," said Maudie.

"In some weeds," said Arthur. "He wasn't hurt bad."

"Unless his head was cracked," suggested Una.

Aunt Fiona grabbed the nearest child, who happened to be Arthur, and shook him hard. "Why didn't you tell me?" she demanded.

"They banged on the top of the cab," recalled Mum. "I thought they were playing."

"We'd better hurry back and get him," said Aunt Blanche. She, Mum and Aunt Fiona climbed into the front, and five of her kids got in the back with us.

Max was nowhere in sight when we got to the place where he had fallen out.

"He's gone," Aunt Fiona said weakly after we had searched all the clumps of bushes nearby.

"Maybe he's dead," whispered Una.

"Hush," said Mum. "If he were dead he'd still be here, wouldn't he?"

We stared at each other silently.

"Remember," said Maudie, sniffing back her tears, "how he never used to cry when he fell and hurt himself? How he'd just suck his thumb all the harder?"

"Remember how he used to just sit and listen when all of us were talking around the fire at night?" Ralph said. "How once he fell asleep by the couch and we forgot he was there and left him all night?"

Georgie broke into loud wails. Violet, one of Aunt Blanche's kids, joined him. "I can't remember which one was Max," she wept.

Aunt Fiona was close to tears herself. "He was the best little boy." She sniffed. "Made me a little birthday card last week all by himself."

"No, Mum," said Leonard. "That was me."

"Well," said Aunt Blanche briskly, "let's not stand here talking about him as if we'd never see him again. Let's all get back in and drive down the road. Maybe somebody picked him up and is looking for us."

"Maybe he's kidnapped," whispered Una, creating another crisis. Faced with thirteen blubbering children, Aunt Fiona shoved us all in the truck and we drove back down the road, peering all along the way for a small boy who sucked his thumb.

"If Max was here," said Ralph as we bounced along, "I would ask him if he was hurt and I'd tell everybody to shut up long enough to hear what he said."

LOOK," cried Una, who was standing up so she could see better, "here comes the police."

We cowered down in the van, since we were all a little afraid of the tall policeman with his dark clothes and stern face.

As the police car drew alongside us, we saw Max sitting beside Constable Smith.

"Maybe it's against the law to fall out," whispered Una.

Constable Smith hailed Aunt Fiona, who stopped the van with a jerk. "Max," she shrieked, tumbling from the cab and almost strangling Max as she hugged him through the open window of the police car.

After a short spell of weeping, she lifted him out, and felt his head for possible injuries.

"We picked him up and brought him to town," said Constable Smith.

Max looked at the ground, sucked his thumb, and said nothing.

"I didn't know whose kid he was," continued the constable. "Said his name was Macth, but didn't know if he had another name. Said he fell out of a big truck full of more people than he could count." Constable Smith looked us over and nodded. "Had to be you."

"He said all that!" exclaimed Aunt Fiona.

"Lady, that isn't all he said," Constable Smith told her. "About talked my ear off. Told me you said his Uncle Archie was a lazy so and so. Said your kids smoked a packet of cigarettes out in the willows yesterday."

We wilted under his gaze.

"Let's see now. He said he didn't think you'd notice he was gone because his Uncle Ellis said you're kind of careless and it runs in the family and that's why you've got so many kids."

"That's enough," snapped Mum. She nodded toward all of us kids who were listening with our mouths ajar.

Aunt Fiona's mouth was ajar, too. "Max said all that?"

The constable nodded. "And more. Talked like he'd never get

BEWARE OF THE CAT

WHOEVER said "Sticks and stones may break my bones but names will never hurt me" was certainly not a cat. Which means they were not very intelligent.

On behalf of all cats everywhere, I stand here to address you lot as a form of protest.

I protest against the staggering lack of tact and imagination which is consistently shown by you lot to us lot on the question of our names.

Just think about it! Look at the usual choice — "Pooh," "Blackie," "Fishface," "Sissy," "Ginger," and so on and so on until one feels close to choking.

Is that really the best we can expect? The limit of your low, exhausted imaginations? Do me a favour!

Look at me — look at your own cat. And ask yourself if the name you have chosen is suitably apt for so noble a creature. Does the name bestowed have a touch of dignity, a ring of aristocracy, a weight of intelligence, a quintessence of uniqueness?

Care to bet on the answers?

I have never been known to answer to it, but I am called "Squiff," or as some even say it, "Squiffey." Charming!

I have therefore decided, and I announce it now once and for all time, that my name from now on shall be Algy Archibald, Earl of The Alley, and I will only answer to that . . . and to the sounds of my food plate being filled.

Cats of the world unite — and refuse to answer to yelps and cries of "Puss-puss — here, pretty puss-puss!"

If you can't choose a name, choose a number. Make it a swinging one!

As we cats say, you only live nine times, you know!

another chance."

Our gazed shifted to Max, who stood tracing a furrow in the dust with his toe while he sucked his thumb and hummed softly.

"Max," said Aunt Fiona. "Are you all right? How do you feel?"

Max looked at her. His eyes shifted to the vast crowd of us children, who looked at him quietly and expectantly. It was probably the first time he'd ever seen us all silent.

Suddenly he removed his thumb from his mouth and shoved his hand into his pocket. A grin split his face.

"Thuper," he said.

*** THE END ***

TOOTY - THE TORTOISE THAT SHOULD HAVE BEEN AN ELEPHANT

THE reason I got a tortoise was because I wanted an elephant.

Not unusual for a child of nine, but my parents were exceptionally conventional and wouldn't hear of an elephant in our suburban back garden.

Being rather a devious child anyway, I'm inclined to think that I had really only wanted a tortoise in the first place, and had started the elephant rumour as a giant red herring. My parents were so relieved.

I read all I could about tortoises, and when we finally found a pet shop that sold them I was able to inform all concerned that the chosen beast was a young Greek female.

With these credentials, we should have called her something like Aphrodite, but we weren't sure that she really looked like an Aphrodite. So we called her Tooty, for short.

She was charming and wilful, showing both characteristics within 20 minutes of leaving the pet shop.

As we got on the bus, her perforated travelling box on my knees, the scrabbling from within grew louder and more insistent until, with a triumphant heave, Tooty thrust her head and shoulders through the lid. She had a good look round and then beamed toothlessly at the conductor.

"You'll have to pay for it," muttured the conductor, retreating hastily behind his ticket machine.

So Tooty received an eightpenny ticket and spent the rest of the journey in style. With her scaly arms hooked over the side of the box and her neck stretched to its limit, she gawped at the other passengers. Occasionally she would turn her head, blink slowly and gulp, giving an impression of reptilian mirth.

She was an amiable reptile, though she ruled us from the beginning. Our chief conflicts grew up over the garden.

My mother was a keen gardener and so was Tooty but not in quite the same way.

Many times, startled neighbours would hear Mother threatening to tear an invisible somebody shell from shell if she didn't get out of the gentians this instant!

SO Mother delivered the first of many ultimatums, and believing that holes in shells were cruel, I built a mobile Tooty pen.

A wooden box with the bottom knocked out seemed to be the answer. Place box over juicy dandelions, place tortoise in box, check adequate shade and jar-lid of water were present, congratulate self and leave.

Return an hour later to move box and — no tortoise. Hastily remove tortoise from gentians and replace in box, wondering how the dickens she managed it.

Tooty obligingly began to demonstrate under our very eyes.

She could climb. Stretched up on tiptoe, she would hook her front legs in cracks, and scrabble madly until

There was nothing slow about Tooty, says J. Drakeford, especially when she was hungry and Mother's favourite flowers were nearby!

she could reach the top of the box. A final heave and a kick and she was poised between heaven and earth to land on the latter with a thump and a wheeze.

Then, without even a pause to get her breath back, she would stomp determinedly off in the direction of the gentians.

Not wanting to deprive her of the sunshine by putting a lid on the box, we covered the top with wire netting. This meant that every 15 minutes or so someone had to go out and turn the tortoise.

No, we weren't cooking her. It was just that, having reached the top of the box, she would try to climb along the wire netting, inevitably lose her grip at some time during the exercise, and land on her back. She was quite helpless in this position, and if left, our tortoise books informed us, would eventually die.

This fact in no way discouraged her, and soon the whole family had organised itself into a Tooty-turning rota.

Before long, somebody went out to turn over the tortoise and — no tortoise. We picked her out of the gentians and she promptly retired into her shell and refused to come out and be reasonable.

CAME the strawberry season, and the gentians, clutching their tattered petals round them, were allowed a respite. We didn't mind Tooty in the strawberries, for she was a far daintier eater than the slugs, and always finished what she started.

Strawberry season was also sunbathing season, and whoever went out in the garden to sunbathe was automatically elected to tortoise watch.

She liked company, and would, once full of strawberries, cuddle next to any ground-level human.

Often, a sleeping sunbather would waken to see a tortoise lying in faithful imitation, head fully extended, arms and legs spread-eagled out on the ground, and eyes shut, her mouth registering a beaky smirk.

Tooty also showed marked suicidal tendencies. In spite of our organised vigils, she would escape at least once a day and go looking for trouble.

We saw her square up to the dog, rescued her from cats, grabbed her out of the bonfire, accidentally forked her on to the compost heap.

She was our friend for a long time, and we were heartbroken when she died during a bitterly cold snap one spring. We buried her under the gentians. She would have liked that.

The End.

EASY DOES IT

This attractive sweater with cable detail on the dolman sleeves is a must for all fashion-conscious ladies!

Materials Required. — Of **Sirdar Country Style Tweed Double Crepe** 7 (8, 8) x 50 gram balls in main colour; of **Country Style Double Knitting** 3 (3, 3) x 50 gram balls in contrast; one pair each of 3¼ mm and 4 mm (Nos. 10 and 8) knitting needles; 4 mm circular needle 80 cm, *31½ inches*, long (if required to accommodate extra large number of stitches); 3¼ mm circular needle 40 cm, *15¾ inches*, long (or set of four).

For best results it is essential to use the recommended yarn. If you have difficulty in obtaining the yarn, write direct, enclosing a stamped addressed envelope, to the following address for stockists: Sirdar PLC, Flanshaw Lane, Alverthorpe, Wakefield, Yorkshire WF2 9ND.

Measurements. — To fit 86 (91, 97) cm, *34 (36, 38) inch*, bust loosely; length — 56 (57, 58) cm, *22 (22½, 22¾) inches;* sleeve seam — 46 (47, 48) cm, *18 (18½, 19 inches.)*

Tension. — 24 sts. and 32 rows to 10 cm, *4 inches*, measured over reversed stocking-stitch using 4 mm needles.

Abbreviations. — K — knit; P — purl; st.(s) — stitch(es); tog. — together; M1 — pick up loop between sts. and knit into back of it; C3F — slip next 3 sts. on to cable needle and leave at front, K3, then K3 from cable needle; cm — centimetres; M — main colour; C — contrast.

N.B. The sweater is knitted sideways starting with the left sleeve.

Figures in brackets ( ) refer to the larger sizes; where only one figure is given, this refers to all sizes.

Left Sleeve.

Using 3¼ mm needles and C, cast on 49 sts. and work in K1, P1 rib for 8 cm, *3¼ inches*, ending with a right-side row.

Next row. — Rib 6, M1, [rib 1, M1] 36 times, rib to end. [86 sts.]

Change to 4 mm needles and with right side facing, commence working cable pattern:

Note: Use 2 separate balls of M and

twist colours on the right side where they join on every row.

1st row. — P34M, with C P1, K1, P4, K6, P4, K1, P1, with M P34.

2nd row. — K34M, with C K1, P1, K4, P6, K4, P1, K1, with M K34.

Repeat these 2 rows 3 times more.

9th row. — P34M, with C P1, K1, P4, C3F, P4, K1, P1, with M P34.

10th row. — As 2nd row.

These 10 rows form cable pattern and are repeated throughout.

Work 14 (16, 18) more rows straight.

Increase one st. at each end of next and every following 4th row until there are 120 sts., then work 3 rows. Increase one st. at each end of next and every alternate row until there are 140 sts., ending with a wrong-side row. Increase one st. at each end of every row until there are 156 (160, 164) sts.

Shape Body.

Cast on 23 (24, 25) sts. at beginning of next 2 rows. [202 (208, 214) sts.]

Work 45 (47, 49) rows straight, keeping cable pattern correct, ending with a right-side row.

Shape Neck.

Next row. — With wrong side facing, pattern 101 (104, 107) sts.,turn, slip remaining sts. on spare needle.

Next row. — Cast off 8 (10, 12) sts., work to end.

Decrease one st. at neck edge on next and every following row until 81 (82, 83) sts. remain.

Work 25 rows straight on remaining sts.

Increase one st. at neck edge on every row until there are 93 (94, 95) sts. on needle, ending at neck edge. Leave sts. on a spare needle.

Return to sts. on spare needle, rejoin C and with wrong side facing, decrease one st. at back neck edge on next 9 rows.

Work in M only on remaining sts. for 33 rows.

Increase one st. at back neck edge on next 9 rows using C for increasing, ending at lower edge of Back. [101 (104, 107) sts.]

Next row. — P92 (95, 98), pattern 9C, cast on 8 (10, 12) sts. in C, pattern across sts. from Front. [202 (208, 214) sts.]

Work a further 45 (47, 49) rows in pattern.

Shape Body And Right Sleeve.

Cast off 23 (24, 25) sts. at beginning of next 2 rows. [156 (160, 164) sts.]

Decrease one st. at each end of every row until 140 sts. remain.

Decrease one st. at each end of every alternate row until 120 sts. remain, then work 3 rows. Decrease one st. at each end of next and every 4th row until 86 sts. remain. Work 24 (26, 28) rows straight in pattern, ending with a right-side row.

Next row. — K6, [K2 tog.] 17 times, [P2 tog.] 3 times, [K2 tog.] 17 times, knit to end. [49 sts.]

Change to C, and using 3¼ mm needles, work in K1, P1 rib for 8 cm, *3¼ inches.*

Cast off loosely in rib.

Front And Back Welts.

Using C and 3¼ mm needles and with right side facing, pick up and K116 (120, 124) sts. along lower edge of Front and Back.

Next row. — Rib 12 (14, 16), rib 2 tog., [rib 3, rib 2 tog.] 18 times, rib to end. [97 (101, 105) sts.]

Continue in K1, P1 rib for 14 cm, *5½ inches.*

Next row. — Cast off loosely in rib.

Neckband.

Using 3¼ mm (short) circular needle (or set of 4) and using C and right side facing, pick up and K44 sts. from centre back, pick up and K24 sts. from left side front, 24 sts. from centre and 24 sts. from right side front. [116 sts.]

Work in K1, P1 rib for 7 cm, *2¾ inches.* Cast off loosely in rib.

To Make Up.

Press work according to instructions on ball band.

Join side and sleeve seams. Fold neckband in half to inside and stitch down loosely.

Press seams.

HEAVE-HO!

While learning to drive last year, I was out practising one day with a neighbour.

Coming to a steep hill, I stopped halfway up to practise hill starts.

Some schoolboys in running vests and shorts came panting up the hill, so I waited until they had all passed, which they did without comment — until the last boy.

He was a lad of about 10, who was obviously having difficulty in keeping up with the others.

Seeing two women in a stationary car, he assumed the worst and, peering through the window, he gasped, "Would you like me to give you a push?"

Who says chivalry is dead?

WE'VE been evicted! I never thought such a thing could happen — but here we are, orphans of the storm, homeless waifs, destitute, cold and starving.

All his fault, of course. I told him several times to tidy up the mess we'd made in raiding the larder. I remember distinctly breaking off from eating some super fillet steaks to tell him so.

He was so busy stuffing himself on best Danish bacon that he didn't bother.

Selfish, that's what he is.

So of course we were found out. After all, you can't expect anyone to believe a mouse ate all that steak and bacon, licked the butter, spilt the sugar, and upset a bag of flour.

I'll spare you the grim details of what

DOUBLE TROUBLE

was said and done to us by someone I'd always thought to be a nice, friendly woman.

That was bad enough. But when I heard all that hammering going on outside the back door, I got really worried.

Was it a gallows being built? I began to wish I'd really memorised the RSPCA phone number for just such an emergency . . .

Anyway, we eventually found out that it was this — this monstrosity. A tin shack!

It's diabolical, that's what it is. Putting little dogs like us in a prison like this. We've gone off people, we have.

This metal eyesore has no blazing coal fire, no thick woolly rugs, no cosy armchairs, no warm beds . . . and no food-filled larders.

To expect two self-respecting dogs like us to live in such a hovel is asking too much. It really is.

So, from tonight, we are putting our plans into operation.

We shall start round about her bedtime and we shall whine, whimper, cry, and sob all night.

The next day, we shall refuse all food (it's going to be an ordeal, I know) and lie around this brokendown slum shivering, apathetic, forlorn and unloved.

I think we should be back at our usual warm spots before the fire by tea-time. She's soft hearted, you see.

And next time we raid the larder, I shall see to it that the evidence is not left lying around — if I have to stop eating for all of two minutes to clobber him into doing it.

Now you'll have to excuse me. It's time to start looking pathetic . . .

Emergency Action

IT'S usually a slow process making friends with one's neighbours on a new housing estate.

People tend to be cautious as they discreetly "weigh up" those around them.

A young couple I know moved into such a new estate recently, and in the first weeks, the young wife found her new neighbours greeting her with the odd remark about the weather — and that was all.

Until the day her two young children disappeared . . .

When they didn't appear for their evening meal, the worried parents began to search the district.

Children they questioned told their parents of the missing youngsters — and suddenly there was a rush of neighbours to join in the search.

Cars were used to cruise round the streets, while other men searched fields and other likely places.

The missing children were soon located at play in a half-built house on the far side of the estate. So all ended happily.

But the "emergency" broke the ice between all the neighbours, and from being a collection of new tenants eyeing each other warily, the estate changed almost overnight into a friendly community.

It would have happened eventually, of course. But two wandering youngsters with a sense of adventure made it happen then.

Their mother still gave them a pretty strong ticking-off, of course. She didn't tell them how grateful she was!

THE VERY PRIVATE WORLD OF MR STARK

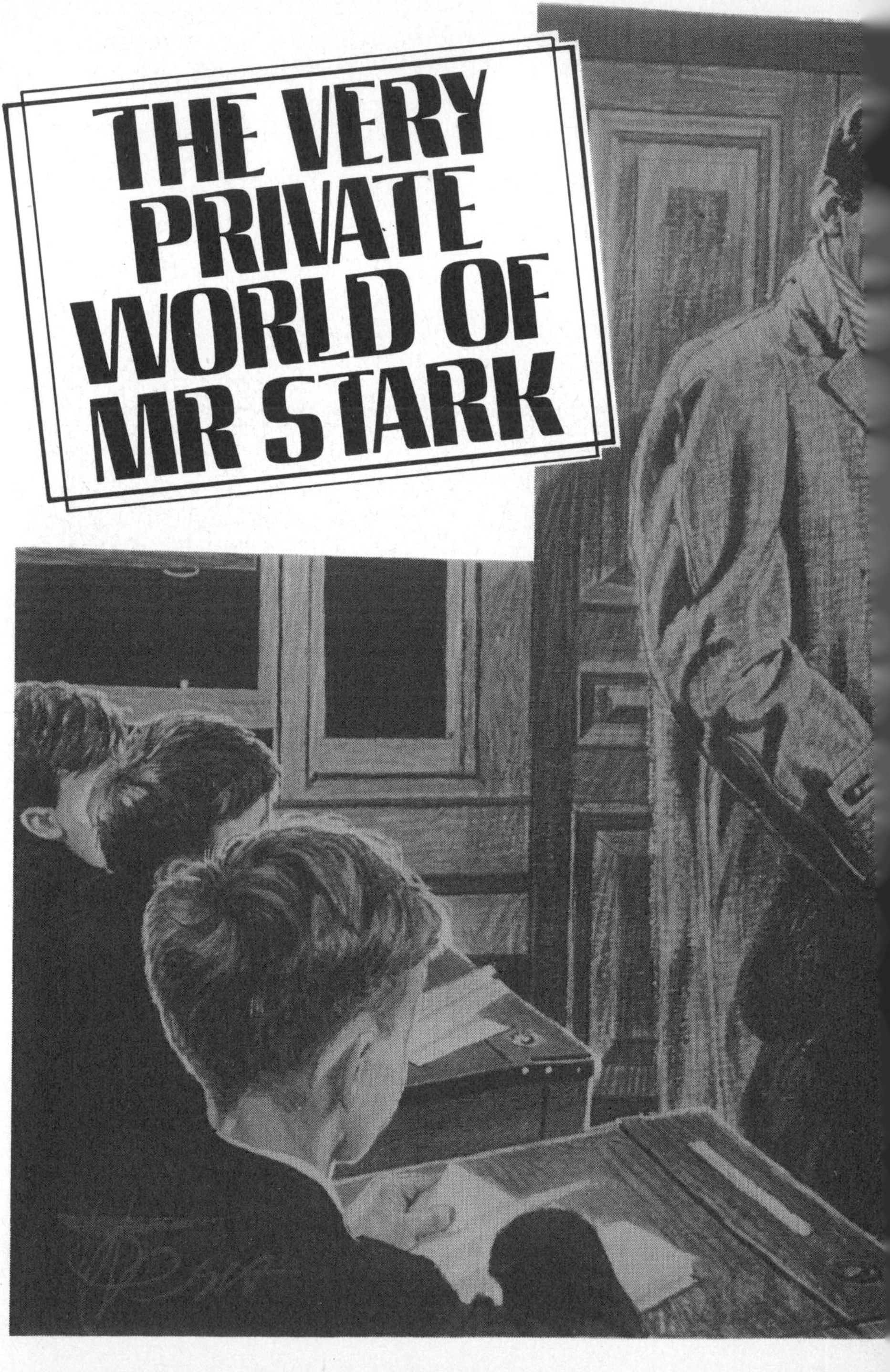

Strangers, when admitted by invitation, came to scoff . . . and stayed to wonder.

Complete Story by MALCOLM WILLIAMS

MR STARK, the acting Headmaster, paused stiffly before the lectern, peered over his spectacles across the sea of young faces, then delivered the final words of his end-of-term address:

"To God our thanks, these closing hours,
For opiate breeze,
Ambrosial showers . . ."

Momentarily, the ranks of the four hundred Junior schoolchildren remained at attention — uncomprehending. Since Mr Stark had been deputising for the regular Head (smitten by lumbago), he'd made a habit of introducing obscure little poems into every assembly.

But he was an obscure sort of man anyway — "very close," as the school secretary described him. Now he took one final look at the gathering and formally called for three cheers. This the children understood — and raised the roof.

The hall doors were opened, summer term was over, and both children and staff poured eagerly out of the hall. Except for Mr Stark — and Eleanor Landimore.

Slowly, Eleanor left the piano stool where she'd been accompanying the singing, and negotiated the whooping, scrummaging pupils in the corridor.

Reaching her classroom, she began checking the last strays among her children, sorting out the usual discrepancies of wrong caps, satchels, shoe bags, bundling out groups of wrestling boys.

Regretfully she smiled her goodbyes in the cloakroom, went into her classroom, closed the door and sat down slowly at her desk.

Wearily she rubbed her temples, raised her head from her hands and stared at the residue of unclaimed lost property on her desk. Eleanor's weariness was an amalgam of nostalgia and loneliness: children filled her life. She would have welcomed endless terms, working weekends. Her heart was heavy and she dreaded the long, empty vacation ahead.

A gentle tap on the door made her look up. A colourful picture in charcoal and chalks hung across the glass partition of the door. Beneath it, a small nervous face peered in. Eleanor stood up and went to open the door.

"Gregory! I thought you'd be home by now," she said in surprise. Gregory was a recent arrival at the school, a diminutive boy. He looked up at Eleanor with sensitive eyes.

"I was wanting to say, 'Have a nice holiday,' miss."

He waited a second for his message to register, then from behind his back he produced a library book and an apple. The apple he polished against his pullover and held it out in offering. "I saved my lunch today, miss. I thought you'd like it."

He seemed pleased with his precise little speech but stood anxiously watching Eleanor. Her eyes softened as she accepted the apple; it was warm from Gregory's covetous clutch.

"Thank you, Gregory," was all she could manage and the boy's nervousness evaporated with a bright smile.

"That's all right then, miss." He hesitated, looking comical with his cap slightly oversize, the peak nearly hiding his pinched little face. "A nice holiday," he repeated, and was gone.

BACK at her desk Eleanor stared at the apple. She forgot her own loneliness as she thought of Gregory. She'd only seen the boy's mother once. Gregory had been playing his recorder at the school concert earlier in the term, not a solo, his thin, sensitive fingers shook too much for a solo performance, too much to do credit to his natural ability.

But his mother hadn't come to watch him perform, she'd merely dropped him off, then stopped at the Headmaster's office to complain that her son had come home with the wrong gym shoes.

Eleanor had tried to talk to her but she'd swept past her in the corridor with her heels clicking, leaving a fog of pungent perfume in her wake.

"Uncle Jim was waiting in the car to take her for a drink," Gregory had explained to Eleanor while waiting for his mother to collect him. "Mum likes going out at night," he'd said loyally. "She gets tired after work, you see."

Eleanor had fretted at the little boy's barely disguised disappointment. He often talked and wrote about his "uncle." He drew pictures of him too and always there was a streamlined car with his mother sitting in the front, brightly made up. Gregory was a talented artist but all his pictures suffered from a significant gap — no father.

The memory made Eleanor snort and sit up. If only Mr Stark had called her in to speak with Gregory's mother. But no, he'd dealt with the case "officially" as he put it. Eleanor resented Selwyn Stark's authoritarian manner. "S.S." the staff had nicknamed him. Ever since he'd taken over from the old Head he'd bound the spirit of the school in manacles.

"You must keep children at arm's length, Miss Landimore," he frequently reminded Eleanor. "Don't get too friendly with them. Dear me, no. They'll eat out your heart!"

Eleanor had just completed her probationary year as a teacher but she had serious misgivings about being confirmed in her appointment. She should have heard something by now but she knew there were complications. She'd only done two terms at her first school.

There had been nothing remarkable about the little village school near her home — except the teacher who took all the gym lessons. Strange that Eleanor had become entangled with him. He'd been the duplicate of Mr Meilen here, same good looks, same arrogance.

But, unlike Mr Meilen, he'd been married. Eleanor had asked for a transfer, but she knew she was really running away, nursing a wound.

BOTTOM'S DOWN!

It was my first attempt at baking a cake and the recipe was foolproof.

"This is easy," I thought, vigorously stirring my gorgeous mixture.

With a flourish I poured it into the waiting cake tin, then moved away to check the oven heat.

On turning round I was appalled to see a sticky mass creeping across the table to land in a large pool on the kitchen floor.

Tears welled up and I wept into the mess.

My beautiful cake was ruined and all because, when greasing the cake tin, I forgot to replace its loose bottom!

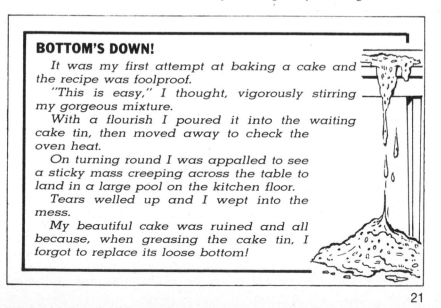

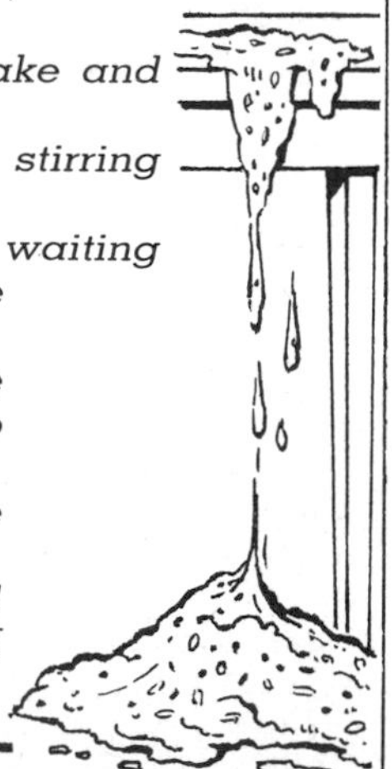

THE door burst open and Eleanor sat up with a start. Mr Meilen and Mrs Taggart breezed in with high humour.

"Not brooding again!" Mr Meilen bawled, striding to the desk. "Term's over, Eleanor, time to relax."

"Time to forsake the little horrors," Mrs Taggart added in relief, her ample matriarchal presence suddenly crowding the room.

"Oh, I just had some clearing up to finish," Eleanor said defensively. She picked up some loose illustrations from the nearest desk and slipped the apple into her cardigan pocket. "I'll be along presently."

"Leave it," Mr Meilen said. "Come on, I'll give you a lift. Leave the school to old 'S.S.' He's still flitting around like a spectre."

"What did you think of his latest choice of verse, Eleanor?" Mrs Taggart asked. She didn't wait for an answer. "Maudlin wasn't the word. Heart like a stone, that man — no time for people. Never brings his wife to school functions. They say he rules her at home with an iron fist!"

"A strange cove," Mr Meilen agreed. "Oh well, things will be sane again when the old Head recovers. I bet 'S.S.' is willing him into retirement . . . sure you won't come, Eleanor?"

She shook her head and started arranging books on the shelves. "I must prepare a few things for next term. I won't have time in the holidays." She was conscious of how false she sounded but nobody noticed.

"Not me!" Mr Meilen said with feeling. "Out of sight, out of mind, that's my philosophy. In twenty-four hours I'll be on the Costa Brava." He slapped his thigh and with a gleam in his eye turned to Mrs Taggart. "And where's the brisk young widow hunting this season?"

"You *are* awful." She giggled, then, for the tenth time, explained to Eleanor.

"I'm doing the fjords this summer. They say there's chance of romance yet for an old one under the Midnight Sun." She winked confidentially. "No harm in hoping!"

ELEANOR waited for their footsteps to die in the corridor before she started locking up cupboards. Unhurriedly she packed some books and charts into her basket and stood giving the classroom a last look. It was very quiet. The electric clock clicked off another minute.

Regretfully she turned round and closed the door behind her.

Except for one car, the school playground was deserted. Eleanor crossed it thoughtfully and had reached the mulberry tree by the school gate before she realised she was being followed. She caught her breath as a shadow crossed her own.

"Gregory!" she exclaimed. "Where did *you* come from?"

He looked up eagerly, large eyes enormous beneath the peaked cap.

"I was hiding behind the milk crates, miss. I ambushed you! You didn't spot me?" He looked pleased with himself, but needed confirmation.

"I certainly didn't." Eleanor looked down at him, almost grateful for being interrupted. She noticed the stains on his shirt collar. "You've been throwing mulberries again, Gregory. Your mother won't be pleased."

"We was having a last game, miss. The other boys told me the mulberries die next term. Anyway — Mum won't mind. The laundry always cleans my clothes up." He felt further explanation was in place. "Uncle Jim don't like Mum doing housework, says it makes her hands rough."

He tapered his own fingers together. "Mum always keeps her nails long and red. I was thinking they weren't as neat as yours though, miss."

He looked down shyly at his shoes as if he'd gone too far, then said, "Uncle Jim bought me these new shoes for being good."

Eleanor put down her basket and squatted to see into the boy's face.

"Gregory, love, why aren't you home having your tea? Your mother will be worried about you. She knows school finishes early today . . ."

"No, miss, I knew Mum would be cross if I came home early. She works at the dress shop in town and I'd have to stay with the lady next door —" He frowned. "I don't like that so I . . . sort of . . . wait about a bit."

Eleanor gripped the boy's shoulders. They felt thin and submissive beneath his pullover. "What time does your mother finish work then?" she asked. "You always have to wait around for her?"

"Oh, it's all right, miss. Mum's in charge of the shop. She's ever so important, miss. She has lots of customers." Momentarily the light of pride burned in his eyes, but then his shoulders dropped again.

Eleanor couldn't resist hugging him. But she was at a loss to know what to do next. This wasn't something that occurred in a classroom situation, this wasn't something they lectured you about at training college!

Mr Stark's voice cracked behind her like a whiplash.

WHY is that boy not out of school?"

Eleanor turned sharply. Mr Stark strode purposefully across the playground towards them. "Why is that boy lingering, Miss Landimore?" Eleanor stood up.

"This boy should have been home long ago," Mr Stark said superfluously. Eleanor bristled, her confusion replaced by indignation. *This boy*, she felt like saying, is a human being, an individual with problems. Instead, she suppressed her temper.

"Gregory is ready to go home now. I'll walk part of the way with him, Mr Stark. Friday traffic starts getting busy about now . . ."

Mr Stark's eyes glinted behind his spectacles. "Let me see, you live on the Newtown estate, don't you, boy?"

Gregory's tongue flicked across his lips. "Yes, sir," he said.

"Your mother's out, I suppose," said Mr Stark, making it sound like an accusation.

"Yes, sir."

"I'll take him home on the bus then," Eleanor suggested, but it was obvious from Gregory's face that he was used to walking home — to kill time.

"No, no, Miss Landimore, that won't do." Mr Stark shook his brief-case against his leg again and peered at his watch. "Dear, oh dear, time's getting on. I'll take the boy home in my car." He paused. "You live across in the old part of town, Miss Landimore, in the *bed-sitter belt*, I believe."

Eleanor looked at him in surprise again. "Why, yes . . ."

Mr Stark was consulting his watch again. "Dear, oh dear, I'll be cutting it fine. I'll drop the boy and then you, Miss Landimore." He turned towards his car, leaving the other two to follow. Eleanor was seething at his condescension. He probably had his head full of some meeting or other . . .

Eleanor would willingly have walked home. Off the school premises her life was her own, but she felt bound to stay with Gregory until he was safely delivered. Mr Stark couldn't begin to understand the little mite's plight . . .

MR STARK handled a car as stiffly as he did children. Traffic was busy and he scowled as they were caught up on the edge of town.

"Dear, oh dear!" he complained while Eleanor sat behind with her basket on her lap. Gregory looked out of the side window, his tongue occasionally moistening his lips.

"Yours is an unusual case, Miss Landimore." Eleanor blinked, meeting Mr Stark's eyes in the driving mirror.

"I beg your pardon?"

"It's unusual for a probationer to do two schools in her first year."

Eleanor nodded, sensing controversy ahead.

A Cry From The Heart

HOW do you talk to a girl when you don't know her?"

That was the question a friend of mine was asked by her 14-year-old son. As she said, he didn't so much ask as cry out in anguish!

Being a wise mother, she took the question seriously. Mother and son began to discuss the important subject of how a young man "chats up" a young lady.

Remembering her own experiences as a shy youngster who longed for good-looking boys to speak to her, my friend suggested this and that.

"Tell her how nice her dress is," she said, "and how pretty she looks in it."

It took her a good 10 minutes to convince him that such an approach was not "soppy" . . . and that the more direct method of "wolf-whistling" was definitely not right!

He was still doubtful. What would the girl say in reply? What would he say then? He wanted it all clean-cut.

And then he dashed off to "chat up" the "dream girl" he was so eager to know . . .

Oh dear, he was back in a very short time, downcast and despairing.

His "dream girl" just didn't want to know him!

It's very difficult learning to grow up — and having to learn two lessons in one day!

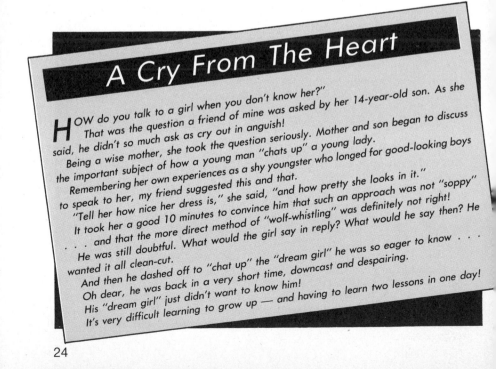

"Yes, I know. My last school let me go on compassionate grounds." She swallowed over the word, her face getting hot. Anyway, what business was this of . . . ?

"Yes, yes," Mr Stark said curtly. "A great pity. One's interests should be undivided during one's trial year. After all, a newly-fledged teacher is virtually a liability until experience takes over . . ."

Eleanor's temper was boiling now. It wasn't often anyone made her see red.

"But don't you think that a novice contributes *something*, Mr Stark? Even if it's only by trial and error! After all, in a journey of a thousand miles the first step is the most important —" She gulped, annoyed with herself for lapsing into platitudes.

"Yes, yes, Miss Landimore, I take your point, but —"

Mr Stark braked dramatically at a red light. Eleanor caught Gregory before his chin hit the front seat. He looked up gratefully, then resumed his vigil at the window. Eleanor wondered how many times he'd been subjected to other adult conversations, how much upset and insecurity he'd been an innocent eavesdropper to . . .

"As I said, Miss Landimore," Mr Stark drove slowly now, seeking the right entry to the precincts of the flats towering ahead, "you must have had — er — problems in such a small village school. The heart is a vulnerable organ and it does tend to dictate to the mind."

Eleanor squirmed. What did "S.S." know of her last school, and her reasons for leaving it?

"Now then, boy, you can navigate from here," he said peremptorily, leaving Eleanor to her thoughts.

GREGORY leaned back and pointed upwards.

"I live up there," he said proudly. "We've got flowers in our window box." He glanced nervously at Mr Stark, who didn't appear to be listening. "Our bell don't work, sir."

Mr Stark stopped examining the array of bell buttons in the entrance porch. "Yes, well, we'd better go in," he said. "Do we walk up, I wonder?"

"There's a lift, sir," Gregory said eagerly, "and I can work it!"

Mr Stark recoiled. "Yes, well . . ."

But Gregory preceded them into the building, beckoning them after him. The lift hummed down and he took over. "You have to stand well back, miss." They stepped inside and Gregory selected the appropriate button.

As they stepped out on the sixth floor they were greeted by the smell of polish and disinfectant — but no-one was about. Gregory hurried along the long corridor as far as his flat and peered through the letter box.

"Mum's not home," he said breathlessly as the others caught up. "I can see her smock hanging up if she's home . . ."

"Do you know *when* your mother will be home, boy?"

Gregory shook his head.

"Well, I won't leave him here, I'll take him back to my flat and bring him back later, Mr Stark," Eleanor said resolutely. "I'll take full responsibility."

Mr Stark looked levelly at her. "It's not a responsibility that devolves on you, Miss Landimore. This will have to be a matter for the Welfare Officer. Meanwhile, I'll have to think of something else."

He fingered his chin and peered at the identical rows of doors. "I'll leave a message for the boy's mother . . ." He fumbled in his waistcoat pocket, extracted a card and wrote a few neat phrases on it, signing it with a flourish. "You don't happen to have a drawing pin, Miss Landimore?"

"I think so." She felt in her cardigan pockets. Among the paper clips and elastic bands in her other pocket she found a drawing pin.

"Splendid! The ever-ready educator," Mr Stark said with a hint of approval. "I'll just pin this here, and then . . . Now, boy, you'd better come home with me. I've notified your mother that I'll bring you back later, so she shouldn't worry — very much. Well?"

Gregory looked startled and glanced at Eleanor for reassurance. Eleanor felt as bewildered as her pupil. "That's kind . . . of Mr Stark, Gregory," she said. "Are you sure, Mr Stark? I feel very responsible, Gregory is one of my . . ."

"Dear, oh dear, Miss Landimore, if we don't hurry I *will* be late!" He inspected his watch with great finality. He was moving away down the corridor when he realised that the other two weren't following. He turned back.

"Well, come along, boy, I haven't all day. You, too, Miss Landimore, you could do with a cup of tea. No doubt you'll be feeling flat — last day of term and everything!"

THERE was a feeling of urgency about Mr Stark's driving this time and soon they were pulling into the drive of a semi-detached house in the suburbs, and gravel churned beneath the tyres as Mr Stark stopped in front of a partially erected garage.

"You must excuse the general untidiness," he instructed Eleanor as they got out. "Not much of my time is my own so I fall behind on chores." He indicated the pile of straw-packed housebricks, the pyramid of builder's sand and a concrete-encrusted wheelbarrow. "Perhaps you'd come to the side door."

Mystified, Eleanor led Gregory to the side porch, which was smothered with clematis. She caught sight of the front lawn, brightened by lupins and a huge magnolia bush; home-constructed trellis work surrounded the house, entwined by gay ramblers.

The picture was entirely out of keeping with Mr Stark's character. Eleanor wondered whose unstinting hand had lent such an idyllic aspect to the place.

She found herself standing in the passage next to Gregory; it was strangely dark for such a bright day.

"If you wouldn't mind waiting a moment, I'll just prepare my wife, Miss Landimore." Mr Stark disappeared into the end room.

Prepare her for the shock, I suppose, Eleanor thought as she heard low voices beyond the door, then her eyes accustomed themselves to the gloom. The passage was darkened by drawn curtains, but along the wall was the biggest aquarium Eleanor had ever seen. Gregory was already entranced, nose against glass.

"Ooooh, miss!" He breathed heavily. "Don't they make our class sticklebacks look sick!"

Eleanor was speechless. The aquarium glowed from a strip of light and a thousand brilliant stripes of tropical fish; guppies, angel fish — she knew only a few names — but she was transfixed by this sudden world of fantastic shapes, extravagant colours.

"Who d'you think keeps them, miss?" Gregory asked, bright eyes following the quick dart of a multi-coloured torpedo across the tank.

"As a matter of fact — *I* do." Mr Stark was standing behind them, peering into the tantalising greenery. "Not a bad colony, if I might say so." He tapped the glass with his fingernail and another torpedo sped away, causing a cascade of fish. "Gives the place an air of tropical splendour," he explained, then remembered Gregory. "I suppose you've seen these in zoos, young man?"

"Oh, no, sir," Gregory said, not taking his eyes off the fish. "I've never been to a zoo."

"Yes, well . . ." Mr Stark turned to Eleanor. "If you'd care to come and meet my wife, she favours the end room. It gets most of the light on that side. The boy can watch the fish for a while." He preceded Eleanor to the door at the end of the passage, held it open for her, and ushered her inside.

The sudden change from gloom to brightness made Eleanor blink, but her surprise arrested her anyway. Mrs Stark sat at the bay window which overlooked the lupins and magnolia bush. Slowly she turned her head and lifted one hand in greeting to her visitor. Eleanor recovered, stepped forward and gently took the hand of the woman sitting in the wheelchair.

A WONDERFUL day," Mrs Stark said later, while her husband was out making the tea.

"I'm afraid I'm to blame for delaying Mr Stark today," Eleanor said, feeling very humble.

"Not at all," Mrs Stark said soothingly, looking at Gregory, who was now sitting upright and silent on a stool clutching book and cap. "How old are you, Gregory?"

He sat up, straighter than ever. "I'm eight, miss — next November. But I can read Top Class books!"

"Would you read to me, Gregory?"

"Can I, miss?" he was asking Eleanor now.

"Of course." Eleanor smiled. "Mrs Stark would love to hear your poems." He was off the stool immediately, but hesitated, wary of the wheelchair.

"You stand beside me, Gregory," Mrs Stark said.

Gregory, reassured, stood close so that they could share the book and began reading his favourite poem. Eleanor rose and went out in search of the kitchen.

"Anything I can do?" she enquired, putting her head round the kitchen door. Mr Stark, in shirt sleeves, spooning tea out of a caddy, reminded Eleanor of her own, easy-going father.

"Ah, Miss Landimore. I'm glad you looked in, I wanted a word with you." He beckoned her inside. "Would you oblige? There are chocolate biscuits in the barrel and cherry cake in that tin. I expect small boys still like cherry cake?"

He was actually asking her opinion, Eleanor thought, as she tipped biscuits on to a plate.

"It's wonderful how Mrs Stark is able to manage," she said cautiously. "I mean, it's wonderful the way you enable her to."

"Maud?" Mr Stark stopped clattering crockery and paused, both hands on the tea cosy as if warming it. "She's got courage, that girl. It's a long time since she was smitten — by the polio, I mean — but her spirit puts mine to shame."

Eleanor found herself looking at a stranger. If "S.S." was an iceberg at school then there was nine-tenths of him unfathomed by his critics . . . Eleanor suddenly felt very callow and her own problems became mere shadows.

"Was that an electric typewriter I saw among all those flowers in the lounge?" she asked.

"Oh, that." Mr Stark smiled to himself. "Yes, I hit on the idea some time ago. Maud can only effectively use her arms, so now she taps away quite happily for hours. She's mad on poetry, composes a lot herself, and the typewriter makes her feel — useful."

"Mr Stark. Do you ever read any of her poems? In assemblies, for instance?"

"Hah!" He suddenly looked very guilty, and boyish. "You've caught me out, Miss Landimore." He smiled, for the first time in Eleanor's experience. "Yes, I must admit I get rather carried away with Maud's verses . . ."

"Like 'opiate breeze, ambrosial showers' . . . " Eleanor prompted him.

Mr Stark nodded. "I suppose they're not entirely suitable for schools, but I'm so proud of them I can't help indulging myself. Do you understand, Miss Landimore? . . . Yes, you obviously do."

HE pushed the trolley as far as the kitchen door, then turned solemnly to her.

"By the way, I'm calling on the Head tonight. Don't worry about your probationary report, it's a good one. In fact, you're quite the most reassuring acquisition we've had at the school for some time!" He nodded in approval, pushed the trolley into the passage and stopped by the aquarium. He tapped the glass again.

"I like to surround Maud with beautiful things," he said. "Painted ladies some of these fish, Miss Landimore, but nevertheless significant. What about the boy's mother, do you think she's just a painted lady?"

Eleanor was astonished by this sudden change of tack. "Well, I hardly know, Mr Stark . . . She did seem rather . . . vivid . . . when I last saw her, but . . ."

"Ah! Don't prejudge. Keep children and adults at bay, Miss Landimore, until you're sure of them, then you can judge. That boy's mother has a problem, she's struggling for survival at the moment, but perhaps we can help — in time, eh?"

"Perhaps starting this evening when we take him back?"

"Splendid! That's what I like, the long view of things. You'll never cure the world overnight, so, *endure* until you can *cure*, eh?" He smiled a second time.

"And talking of bright things, would you care to — er — call on us again in the holidays?" His face creased in relief as Eleanor nodded.

"I'd love to come again, very much."

"Splendid." Mr Stark rubbed his hands and pushed the trolley as far as the lounge door. "That young chap seems to have captivated Maud," he said, bending to listen at the door. "If he's reading her poetry *he'll* have to come again, too." He straightened and with his hand on the handle said:

"I know Maud would *so* love to have you come again, Eleanor. I've talked about you before, what with that upset you had at your first school. Dear, oh dear, pain seems only to assail the nicest people. Shall we go in?"

As he opened the door and pushed the trolley inside, Eleanor's fingers closed over the apple in her cardigan pocket. Her eyes were full, and as she stepped forward she knew that the long vacation ahead was going to be very full, too . . .

As a teacher, her education was only just beginning.

THE END

A Woman's Place

"In the home!" her husband said firmly. "At my job!" she retorted. And so the trouble started . . .

Complete Story by PEGGY JONES

LEONIE SHORE played nervously with her handbag as the taxi sped her homewards to the beautiful flat she shared with her husband Martin.

And "shared" was absolutely the correct word. Leonie had paid for exactly half its furniture and fittings, and the rent, together with all the other bills, was paid from the fund to which she and Martin contributed equally.

Though it looked as if Leonie would be in a position to contribute two-thirds from now on. And that meant only one thing — trouble ahead!

Martin hadn't wanted her to go on working when they married. But she'd fought hard for her job before she'd met him. She loved it and did it well, and didn't see any reason for giving it up.

She disliked housework and cookery and Mrs Masher did it all so much better than she would ever have done anyway.

She sighed as the taxi drew up before the luxury apartment block. If only Martin would see it her way . . .

It would be a good idea, she decided, to soften the blow of her new promotion as much as possible. Before Martin arrived home she would change into something clinging and feminine, pour drinks and await his return in an aura of charm and French perfume.

She was just about to put her key in the front door when it opened and there stood her husband.

"Martin," she said, surprised, "what are you doing home so early?"

"Things," said Martin briefly, and kissed her on the cheek.

He took her hand and led her into the dining-room. There was soft music playing, drinks already poured.

"Sit down, my darling," he said. "I have news for you."

"Good news?" asked Leonie suspiciously.

"Well, half and half, I would say," he said judiciously. "How's your drink?"

"Fine, fine. Go on." In her nervousness she drank half a glassful straight off and coughed.

Martin fussed about her, patting her back, but his eyes held amusement.

"Must have overdone the gin a bit," he said. "Better now? Strong enough to take the news?"

Leonie nodded.

"Mrs Masher's left us," he said.

LEFT us? What do you mean? I saw her this morning and she was perfectly happy then. She didn't say a word to me about leaving."

"I know. She was afraid to. She thought you'd try to persuade her to stay."

"We must get her back. Where's her phone number?"

He shook his head. "Now listen. Mrs Masher is going up north to live with her daughter. She's tired of working."

"But why . . . ?"

"She asked me if I could see her this afternoon," Martin went on, "and I came home early from the office. She told me all about it and I gave her my blessing and a present from us both."

"And fixed it all up behind my back?"

"I did not. She's terrified you'd keep on at her to stay and that she'd finally give in."

He re-filled her glass, lifted his and said, "So, here's to a Masher-less household."

"I suppose you know it's next to impossible to get a woman to help in the house nowadays?" said Leonie, wondering if any of her friends had a treasure she could lure away.

"Yes," said Martin cheerfully, "so how about you being the woman-around-the-house for a change?"

"I knew that was coming," said Leonie. "I'd take quite a large bet that you encouraged Mrs Masher to go."

"You'd lose," said Martin quietly. "I know better than that. I just thought I'd suggest you giving up your job for the umpteenth time — just for the laughs, of course."

Leonie looked down into her glass.

"I've some news for you, too, Martin," she said. "Helen Burge is going to America and they've offered me her job."

"And you've accepted it?"

She met his eyes and nodded. "Well, it's nearly twice as much money and what I've always wanted."

Martin stood up, towering above her.

Leonie felt a little frightened, and more so when he put out his hand and pulled her none too gently to her feet and stood her in front of him like a penitent schoolgirl.

"Sometimes I wonder if you really did say and mean 'love, honour and obey' on our wedding day," he said.

His eyes weren't hard, only a little sad and wondering.

"I crossed my fingers as I said 'obey'," she admitted.

"You what?"

"Well, I knew I would always love and honour you but I really couldn't be sure about the 'obey'."

"What a woman!" He sighed and put his arms round her and kissed her.

"All right," he said. "But don't think I've given up, because I haven't."

LEONIE spent the next afternoon with Helen Burge learning about the new job. At about half past five she rang Martin's office to explain she might be late home, and was told, to her surprise, he'd left early.

And so she rang the flat.

"Hello," answered a woman's voice, with a slight intriguing lilt.

"Er, um," said Leonie, at a loss.

"Can I help you?" asked the voice.

"I've got the wrong number," said Leonie. "My apologies."

She dialled again — and again heard that fascinating feminine "Hello."

She went back to Helen Burge's office.

"I think I'd better go home," she said. "I'll be in early in the morning."

"Don't worry," Helen said. "You know it nearly all anyway."

"Do I?" said Leonie. "I'm beginning to wonder."

When she reached home, she put her key in the door with a trembling hand. In the hallway she stopped. That exotic flower arrangement hadn't been on the table this morning, neither had the floor been as shiny as it was now.

And what was that interesting smell coming from the kitchen . . . ?

As she moved towards the kitchen door it opened and there stood a girl who could only be described as "stunning."

"Good evening," she said. "You must be Mrs Shore. I am Astrid."

"Er, good evening," said Leonie.

"Mr Shore will not be long. He went to fetch champagne."

"Champagne?"

"To celebrate." Astrid spoke clearly and patiently as if to a backward child. Leonie's gaping amazement obviously did nothing to alter her impression.

"I must go back to the kitchen," said Astrid. "Mr Shore showed me how you like your drink and it is on the little table by the window."

Leonie went into the bedroom and hung up her coat. She noticed that the room had been dusted and the mirrors polished.

The bedroom door opened and Martin slipped in and shut it hastily behind him. He put a finger to his lips.

"Hush," he said, "we mustn't upset Astrid."

"Mustn't we?" asked Leonie.

"No. You know how difficult it is to get help in the house and we must treat her like one of us."

"Suppose you tell me all about it?" suggested Leonie.

ALL SYSTEMS GO!

Recently my mother sat her driving test. Nervously she got into the car and prepared herself for the examination.

When her examiner arrived, she looked in the mirror, glanced over her shoulder, changed from neutral into first gear, looked into the mirror again, then over her shoulder, and prepared to take off the hand brake.

Just then, the examiner exclaimed in a loud voice, "It might be advisable to turn on the engine."

Believe it or not she passed!

"You haven't looked so mad for ages," Martin said interestedly. "There are little spots of colour in your cheeks and your eyes are flashing."

He advanced on her and she tried to push him away, but his arms wound round her and the bedroom wall behind her stopped her from retreating further.

And then Leonie heard a soft swish of skirts and there stood Astrid enquiringly in the doorway.

"I knocked several times," she said. "Dinner is ready."

"Thank you, Astrid," said Martin, with dignity, and a little wave of greeting with the arm which wasn't clutching Leonie. "We'll be right there."

Astrid vanished and Martin turned back to Leonie and finished his interrupted kiss.

Then he said:

"Come on, I'm hungry. I bet Astrid's dinner's better than Mrs Masher's meat and two veg."

THE meal which Astrid served was undeniably delicious. She brought the dishes in, set them on mats and they each helped themselves. They drank the champagne and made polite conversation.

Much as she wanted to, Leonie could not openly question Astrid. All she learned was that she was working her way round the world, living temporarily in a girls' hostel and liking it very much, thank you.

After the meal Martin insisted on helping Astrid with the washing-up and then drove her back to the hostel. Leonie was left alone to contemplate the fact that she had a battle on her hands.

A girl as lovely as Astrid was potential dynamite, she realised. And when you added her cooking ability and housewifery to her beauty the result was positively lethal. No husband would, or could, be immune.

Martin returned, smiling.

"What a smasher," he said appreciatively. "Discussed our political situation with me all the way to the hostel. Knows more about it than you do, old girl, and she doesn't even belong here."

"You can say that again," said Leonie.

Martin went blithely on.

"Snatched her right from under old Watterson's nose," he said. "He'd arranged for her to come over and everything, but I just offered her double money, and as she had no contract with the Wattersons, she agreed to come here right away. Said she liked my face."

"I bet," said Leonie. She liked Martin's face herself. Very much.

"I've told her she needn't come in until about ten in the morning," Martin said. "We only ever have toast and coffee for breakfast and there's no need to drag her over here early just for that."

"Of course not. Mustn't overwork her."

Leonie's sarcasm went quite unnoticed.

The next morning they both left home at the usual time but Leonie made the excuse of having to return for her gloves and Martin went on alone.

When Astrid arrived at ten o'clock, Leonie was sitting waiting for her. They greeted each other politely.

"Now," said Leonie, "I'm going to ring Mr Watterson and tell him that it was all a mistake, that you didn't mean to let him down and that you're going round to his house right away."

"But . . ." said Astrid.

"No buts," said Leonie, and dialled Mr Watterson's number. Astrid sat and waited, composed and beautiful and highly irritating.

"Well, well," said Mr Watterson. "I didn't expect it to work quite so quickly but we'll be jolly glad to have Astrid back. Didn't really want Martin to borrow her at all. Missed her no end."

"I beg your pardon," said Leonie.

"Don't you worry," rambled on Watterson, "you'll soon get used to doing the housework. Martin's convinced you've only to give it a try, and he's right. You'll see."

Leonie put down the receiver. Astrid smiled.

"Well, I go back to them now," she said. "A pity. I had a whole week's menus planned. I did not think I should need more but, see, I over-estimated."

The door closed behind her.

After kicking a couple of cushions across the room, Leonie sat down thoughtfully. It was no longer just a matter of her job. All she could think of was that Martin wasn't going to win. She wasn't going to stay home and stagnate.

He returned that evening, smiling and assured, and looked round for Astrid.

"I rang Mr Watterson," said Leonie. "And he gave the game away. She's gone back to look after him and his family."

"So?" said Martin, his face falling.

"You're the fixer," said Leonie. "You fix this."

"Right," said Martin, rapidly recovering. "One of us has to stay home and look after the flat. You won't, so it'll have to be me!"

NEXT morning Martin rose, tied his dressing-gown firmly about him, made coffee and toast and then began examining the contents of the refrigerator and making a shopping list.

"You can't mean it," Leonie said.

"Oh, but I do!"

"You're just going to look foolish. What will people say?"

"I won't worry," said Martin. "I'll be safely hidden away in my little kitchen. I won't hear them. You will."

Martin could boil eggs beautifully, grill steak to perfection and toss a fine salad. Unfortunately that was all he could do, and after three days the diet began to pall.

On Saturday Leonie looked out a wedding present cookery book and served up a reasonable Hungarian goulash. On Sunday she noticed that the carpets were fluffy and the bookshelves dusty and got out the vacuum cleaner and a duster.

Strangest of all, she found an odd satisfaction in making the room bright and shiny.

"So my housekeeping's not good enough for you?" said Martin.

"When are you going back to the office?" asked Leonie.

"Depends on you," said Martin. "They'll get by without me, and I'm enjoying being chained to the kitchen sink. No more nasty decisions to take. No irate clients to calm down. Wonderful."

On Monday Leonie went to the office in a very subdued frame of mind.

"What washing do you want doing today?" Martin shouted after her as she went down the stairs. She caught a glimpse of his grin as she shuddered.

That evening Leonie gave in.

She silently ate a boiled egg followed by steak and salad and then said, "OK, you win. I handed over to my assistant today and as the case was urgent they accepted my immediate resignation."

"Darling," Martin said, leaping round the table to kiss her. "You won't regret it. I promise you."

She kissed him goodbye next morning and waited at the window until he turned the corner. Then she went into the bedroom, picked up the executive brief-case she'd never need again, and burst into tears.

THAT evening, Martin returned home carrying a large bunch of flowers and looking very pleased with himself.

"Well," he said. "And how's my little housewife?"

"All right," said Leonie sadly.

"Only all right?"

"Yes, I'm sorry, but that's all I can honestly say."

"Just as well, considering the two bits of news I have for you. I've been very busy today on your behalf."

"Have you?" asked Leonie, and darted anxiously into the kitchen, from which came an ominous smell of burning.

"Astrid has a cousin," said Martin, leaning in the kitchen doorway and watching her frantically wave a steaming saucepan about. "A nice plain girl," he added.

"She wants to come over here to work the same as Astrid, but only part-time, so she can study as well. I don't suppose you're interested?"

"Oh, Martin," breathed Leonie, putting the saucepan down on the table.

Martin moved it to safety and went on:

"And that Managing Director of yours is an awfully nice chap. Agreed like a shot when I said you'd like to go on working but only half-time. He said half-time with you was worth more than full-time with anyone else."

Leonie threw herself into his arms. Martin stretched round her and turned off the gas before holding her tightly and kissing her.

"Oh thank you, thank you, darling," said Leonie.

"And thank you," said Martin. "I know how much it cost you to give up your job."

"I cried like mad this morning," she said honestly.

"I know. I know. Now, you just sit there and I'll cook eggs and steak and . . ."

Leonie smiled.

"And I'll toss the salad," she said. ■

—— * **THE END** * ——

"When I Smell Flowers, I Know Something Is Going To Happen"

The scent of flowers where no flowers exist, ghostly touches, coloured lights — Mrs N. takes them all in her stride because, to her, they are part of a wonderful gift she has for seeing into the future.

EVEN as a very small child, I was very conscious of different smells. I can remember being in a pram and smelling the hot leather as the sun's rays beat down upon it.

By the time I was 10, I had already begun to associate lilies with funerals. I never cared for their perfume, it seemed to haunt me.

One day, in my parents' front room, just before my 10th birthday, I suddenly smelt the strong odour of lilies and felt uneasy.

Later, I smelt them again in my grandmother's house. There were no lilies present at either time.

About three days later, my grandfather, whom I loved dearly, came home from work, commented on how cold it was outside and died suddenly of a heart attack.

From then on, until I was about 16, I often smelt lilies just before the death of someone I knew. Then, quite suddenly, it left me.

Later, when I had married, I moved to another town. I felt urged to go and explore spiritualism and went to a meeting. I was told that I was a "born medium."

I had no idea then what a "born medium" was, but I started to attend regularly to find out more.

In a matter of weeks I began to see the most beautiful colours or lights in the most unexpected places. In the bathroom, in cupboards and in the streets. I even saw them on people's faces and their bodies.

They were of various shades ranging from deepest purple to light shades of blue. I saw gold lights, pink lights, amber lights, white lights and some that were a mixture of different colours.

At first I put this down to optical illusion, but after a while I realised these lovely colours were not of this world. Then the smells began again. This time they were the most beautiful perfumes one could imagine.

Each time I looked about me for

soaps, talcum powder, and anything scented, but there were none in my vicinity.

Walking along the street I could smell them as though I were surrounded by bouquets of flowers, I smelled them in a smoky car and in buildings where there were no flowers present.

They came around me many times when I was exhausted and the result was like receiving a tonic to revive me.

Then one day, when I was in a certain worrying situation, I heard a voice at my elbow say, "It's enough to make a cat laugh." I'd only ever known one person to use this phrase — my grandfather. And he had been dead nearly 20 years.

After that, I no longer doubted that I had a gift of extra-sensory perception. I took lights, scents and voices in my stride and they became a part of my everyday life. I began to note that after seeing certain lights certain events would happen.

A dark blue light always prepared me for a windfall. I won a little money only a day after seeing it!

However, greenish-blue light always means that something I'm counting on won't happen. I've proved this many times.

To this day I have not solved the meanings of all the lights I see. One is always learning from them and it would take years to know the meaning of them all.

However, one day I saw one pink light and one cream light on the shoulder of a young woman. I knew her quite well, so I was able to ask her a fairly personal question.

"Are you by any chance adding to your family?" I said.

"Good Lord, no," she replied. "One is enough at the moment."

I did not say any more at the time and didn't see her for about six months. The next time I met her she was sitting by our local river one afternoon, very obviously pregnant.

When she saw me she laughed about it and recalled what I had said to her. I replied that the baby was not one baby but two!

The twin lights I had seen made me sure of it. Shortly afterwards she gave birth to a boy and a girl.

MY experiences aren't only confined to lights and smells. Sometimes I feel "touches" on my face, my hair, my head and my body.

If all other extra-sensory perception could be explained away as imagination, how could one possibly feel unseen fingers touching one's body?

If I am day-dreaming or messing about wasting time and I feel a poking in my ribs, I know that I am to get a move on as I am going to be on call about something.

Sometimes it is a visitor. I have even heard "A visitor for you," spoken in words at the same time.

When at one point I suffered from insomnia I found myself being "persuaded" to lie quietly and see what happened. I felt this sensation of cold, like "electric rain" being poured upon my head which seemed to "shrink" away the overheating in my brain.

Then my head and face were "stroked," bringing with it a sense of drifting into sleep. I truly wish this could be given to everybody who suffers from insomnia.

A similar form of healing comes when I am unable to lie down and relax. Even when sitting upright I can feel this same "freezing" sensation.

Many a headache has been cured in this way. I find myself yawning and even sneezing. My eyes run with water and I come out of it most refreshed.

One day, knowing this "power" was with me, I offered to lay my hands on a young woman who was suffering terribly with a bad head due to sinus trouble.

I drew my hands gently across her brow, head and face for about five minutes, and the headache was soon gone. She thanked me after it was over and told me she felt ready to drop off to sleep!

Since then, although a bit shy at putting myself forward, and not always knowing how to approach the subject, I have offered this healing on head conditions from time to time with excellent results.

The wonderful thing about these gifts is the way one is enabled to help other people — often to help themselves.

If I get a "whirring" feeling in my solar plexus, I know that some dangerous ground is being trodden on — either literally or figuratively speaking.

FOR instance, last summer my sister and her husband decided to take my brother and my father to the sea for the weekend. My father

was 80 and for days I worried that the journey might be too much for him. This feeling grew daily until I felt the whole business was unwise.

Finally, as I don't live near, I telephoned my other sister asking her to intervene and get the trip cancelled.

However my advice was ignored. The journey went forward as planned, and all went well until the journey home.

At exactly halfway, the car broke down and had to be abandoned. They all had to walk two miles to the nearest garage which they found to be closed.

When the party finally arrived in town, the last bus had gone, and they arrived home by taxi, completely exhausted.

Although I have undeniable gifts of extra-sensory perception, I do not have fewer problems than other people.

But almost daily I have cause to be grateful for being shown how to tackle them. □

To her husband, she thought, she'd always been second best. She wasn't the bright and beautiful Vivian he'd loved, but the plain Janet he'd married.

SECOND BEST

IT was Cathy, at the breakfast table, who first told Janet the news.

"Mum, do you know a Vivian Gordon?"

Janet Cartwright put down her fork. "What did you say?"

"Vivian Gordon." Cathy shrugged. "At least that was her name once. She married an American seventeen years ago and went off to the States. She must have been about your age, Mum. I thought you might have known about her."

"Yes." Janet glanced quickly at her husband, but he was staring at his plate. "I did. She was a friend of mine."

"Well," Cathy went on, "her husband's dead. She's coming home for good."

"Oh."

"Don't know what her name is now she's married — Barrs or Bowes or something. Has a daughter, too . . ."

"Cathy." Alan's voice was suddenly firm. "If you're running in the village gossip stakes you'll pip everyone at the post. Isn't it time you were off to school?"

Cathy pouted, then grinned. "All right." She swallowed the remains of her coffee and turned to her younger brother and sister. "Come on, kids."

Janet shepherded her family into the hall, found books and satchels, helped with the coats, and stood in the doorway waving them goodbye.

She closed the door as Alan came into the hall. Should she mention it? Could she afford not to? She drew a deep breath and said: "So Vivian's back?"

"Yes." Alan was already turning away. "I'll be off now, Jan. I'll be working in the top field. See you, darling . . ."

"See you," she echoed. He kissed her lightly and went through the door, leaving her with the sinking feeling that was the forerunner of fear.

The thing she had dreaded for so many years was to be brought into the open at last. Perhaps it would be a good thing. At least, she'd know . . .

She dumped the pots in the sink and swirled water on to them absent-mindedly.

Vivian Gordon, my friend . . .

SHE wondered vaguely why they had been friends. Possibly because they lived in the same village, and were of an age. There could be no other reason, they were so completely different.

Vivian, with her shining dark hair and attractive face. "The most popular girl in the school," Miss Briggs, the house-mistress had said. Top of the form, a good leader, excellent at games, what couldn't Vivian do?

The two girls had travelled together every day on the bus to Brampton

Complete Story by JOYCE BELL

High, where Janet, a borderliner who had just scraped in, soon gravitated to the bottom.

"Why can't you be like your friend?" Miss Briggs had asked. "She's a credit to the school." Even the Head had smiled on Vivian.

But Janet hadn't envied Vivian, not then. That came much later, when Miss Briggs was left behind. Unless there had been a touch of envy in the mammoth sense of inferiority Vivian had aroused in her . . .

She left the pots and walked to the mirror in the corner. Her hair was short, straight and untidy. She never had time to get it done. Or was that true? Could she not spare a morning occasionally from the farm and the children and Alan?

Viv's hair had always shone. Even on the hockey field she had looked well groomed. "Oh, well," Jan told herself. "Either you have it or not."

Together the two girls had struggled into their teens. Janet's figure had become lumpy and her school tunic had bulged unbecomingly. Her face was spotty. Vivian had merely become nicely rounded, her complexion clear.

At 16 they had gone separate ways. The Head had thought firmly that Jan was not really up to university standard, and had suggested a commercial course. Vivian went on to be Head Girl. She was going to teach.

They still came home on the same bus, but now Vivian sat with Alan. And then the envy had started, for Janet loved Alan. She had sat miserably in the back seat watching the two heads so close together, the dark shining one and the one she loved.

Alan had gone to agricultural college. Vivian to university. Before she went, Alan had placed a ring on her finger.

Vivian had taken her degree but she'd never become a teacher, never even come home. The startled village had heard that she was going to America with this man Barrs or Bowes. And Alan had walked around with misery in his eyes.

And then she, Janet, had done something which, even now, made her face burn with shame. She had asked him — *asked him* — to accompany her to a local dance.

And that hadn't been all. After that, she had suggested they meet again and had finally married him. On the rebound, didn't they call it?

But I loved him. I was sorry for him, she thought. I wanted to help him, he looked so unhappy.

Yet the doubt was still there and the sadness. And the knowledge that Alan hadn't asked her first . . .

And now they were married. They were happy with three fine children. But the same question nagged her. *Did he really love her as he'd loved Vivian?*

Janet wondered what Vivian would look like. Seventeen years was a long time. Janet looked at her own thickened figure, her roughened hands, the streaks of grey in her hair. Would Vivian be fat, or too thin, or have wrinkles . . . It was hard to imagine.

She tackled the pots firmly. I'll soon know, she thought. I'll soon know everything.

THE days passed and nothing was said. Alan came in from the fields, tired, and sat in the armchair and read the newspaper as he had done for so many years.

Cathy kept them informed. Vivian would be home on the 24th, with her daughter. "The same age as I am," Cathy said. "I'll have a new friend."

On the 23rd, Janet had made an appointment for a hairset and rinse, but young Pat had a feverish cold and she couldn't leave her. She washed it herself as usual.

That night before she went to bed, she sat at the dressing-table covering her face with cold cream.

"What on earth are you doing?" Alan asked.

"Trying to improve my complexion," she said lightly.

He grunted. "What's wrong with your complexion? Come to bed, I have to get up early. Blossom's due to calve in the morning."

She wiped off the cream, wondering how Vivian would have run the farm. She was a farmer's daughter, after all.

That night she dreamed of rows and rows of shining electric milkers, and cows who calved when they were told. Miss Briggs stood in the background saying, "Vivian will make a success of whatever she attempts."

She woke with a headache, burnt the toast, scalded her hand, almost

forgot to feed the chickens, rang for the vet for Blossom, took Alan a hot mug of coffee to the barn, then ran out to the chemist's to get Pat's prescription. On the way back she met Vivian.

She was talking to the vicar's wife, who turned as Janet approached. "Ah!" She beamed. "I'll leave you two to talk."

Janet stood before Vivian, and suddenly she was 12 years old again, looking humbly at the clever girl who had such high marks in all the exams. She was 17, watching the pride of the Sixth sit with Alan in the old bus.

Vivian looked just the same. Janet pushed the hair out of her eyes and wanted to cry. Was it possible that a woman could be so unchanged after so many years? Was it fair?

Vivian was still slim. She wore a grey wool dress and matching coat, quiet yet in perfect taste. Her dark hair was as shining as ever.

Beside her stood a tall lanky girl, who made her mother seem all the more attractive.

"Janet, dear," Vivian said. There was the faintest touch of an American accent now, and as she smiled Janet saw two tiny lines, so small as to be almost unnoticed. Two lines in 17 years . . .

"Hello," Janet said. "I was sorry to hear about your husband . . ."

"Very sad for us," Vivian agreed. "He worked so hard." She sighed. "But it's wonderful to be back."

"Yes." Janet opened her mouth to speak again, but Vivian was running on.

"I should have come over on a visit. Gerry wanted me to — begged me sometimes — 'You want to see your folks' — but I couldn't leave him. He always had another store to open, and this meant travelling. I had to go with him."

She broke off, giving the impression that there was much more that could have been said. "I — that is — we couldn't let go a moment."

"No," Janet said.

"This is my daughter, Melanie. Say hello, Melly."

"How do you like England?" Janet managed to say.

The girl opened her mouth, but Vivian intervened. "She'll love it when she's been here longer. I want her to get into a good school where she can prepare for university entrance. I'd like her to go to Oxford.

"She'll have to work very, very hard, though. But she takes after her father's family and they all had to work."

"Oh?" Janet asked politely.

"Not that it worried Gerry. There's great opportunity in the States if you're willing to work."

Janet looked down, feeling untidy, clumsy, incompetent, as she always had when faced with Viv's brilliance. She forced herself to listen to the next words.

"I'm giving a little party tomorrow night for a few friends. Will you and Alan come?"

There could be so many excuses, but she could never tell them to Vivian. A sick cow, unfed chickens, housework not quite finished, in short, muddle and incompetence.

"I'll have to ask him," she said at last.

"But you must come, I want to see everyone again. Everyone." She turned her head. "I'll have to go now, Janet. So nice to have met you. We'll see you tomorrow."

"If Alan can make it," Janet said feebly.

THAT evening she told Alan about the invitation. She thought he hesitated just a second before saying easily, "Why not? I'll go if you want to."

I don't, Janet thought, but knew she must. Knew that sometime in the next few days she must lay this bogey to rest once and for all.

They dressed for the party in silence. Janet put on her nicest dress, made up her face, brushed her hair. Then, to give herself courage, she added scent behind her ears and a rhinestone necklace which had been a present from Alan's mother.

Immediately she entered the other farm she felt overdressed. Vivian came to meet them in another simple, well-cut dress with no ornament at all, nothing but her shining hair and flawless, almost undetectable make-up.

There were quite a few people there, and they all stared as Alan shook hands with Vivian. All remembering, no doubt.

Janet caught the look of incredulity on Alan's face as he looked at Vivian. So he'd noticed how young she looked — just like the girl he used to love.

Vivian's mother, a quiet woman in her sixties, brought in plum-cake and elderberry wine. Her brothers, quiet countrymen, stood around her. And Vivian told them about America.

It's interesting, Janet thought guiltily as they passed from California to Utah, with Barrs' or Bowes' stores all the way. It's just that I'm not used to addressing a crowd of people, I never have been. She saw Melanie's eyes on her and smiled guiltily again. She'd only just noticed the child.

How she did stoop. Really, I'd be quite worried if it were Cathy, Janet thought. She looked pale, too. So unlike Vivian.

"It's so wonderful to be back," Vivian was drawling. Like a visiting film star, Janet thought, and knew her bogey wasn't laid yet. Tonight she'd have to ask Alan, and if he told her what she dreaded hearing she'd hate Vivian for the rest of her days.

Janet was shocked at her own vehemence. Vivian was a nice person. Everyone thought so. Even Alan. He was listening eagerly, still with the fascinated look on his face.

WHEN they rose to go Janet was glad. She was tired of the warm room and the scent of her own perfume, and most of all she was tired of not knowing.

They didn't say much on the way home. When they got in, they took off their coats and sat before the fire. Cathy had put the younger children to bed and Janet felt a sudden rush of affection for her eldest daughter.

She turned to Alan.

"What do you think of Vivian?" she asked, amazed at how casual she'd made the question sound.

He pursed his lips. "She certainly can talk, can't she?" he asked warily.

"Viv always was a great talker," she said.

"Did you hear that bit about farming in the U.S.? She certainly knew it all."

"I'm afraid I didn't listen to everything," Jan said guiltily.

"She did go on. And her voice was like a saw."

Jan stared. "You didn't — like her?" she asked.

Alan looked puzzled, and she went on. "Oh, Alan, I must know. After all, you did love her once. You've never told me . . ."

"Told you what?"

"If you're glad you married me."

"What's this?" Alan asked. "Do I have to tell you that? What have I done?"

"Nothing, Alan. Not you. But you did love Vivian. You've never said how hurt you were when — when she . . ."

"When she went off with that American chap? I suppose I was upset at the time, I was only twenty-one after all, and no-one likes being dropped like that. And she was a pretty girl."

"Yes." Janet drew a deep breath. "Alan, did you really want to marry me?"

He looked puzzled for a second then threw back his head and laughed. "You really are a dumbo, Jan. Your father didn't have a shot-gun at the wedding, as I recall."

Janet shook her head and rubbed her fingers together nervously. "But that time, Alan, when I asked you to the dance . . ." She broke off, unable to meet his eyes.

"Dance?" he asked. "I don't remember." He laughed. "I bet you didn't pay."

He had forgotten.

"I have always felt guilty about it, Alan," she said more boldly.

"You see, I'd always loved you." She'd never told him that before. "And then, as soon as Viv went I just chased you."

He was looking at her thoughtfully. "I remember now," he said, "thinking how different you were."

"You see," she said, "I must know, Alan — if you wished you'd married Vivian instead of me."

"I think," he said deliberately, "I had a happy release."

"Alan!"

"Well, didn't I? Vivian's standards are too high for me. Looks as though they were too high for the poor chap she married too. He flogged himself to death trying to keep up. That girl of hers, too, doesn't look at all strong to me. Not fit for the rat-race of university intake and whatever. Vivian forgets that most people can't keep up with her."

But why does she always choose people who can't keep up with her? Janet asked herself. And for the first time she realised why Vivian had wanted her for a friend.

"If I hadn't wanted to marry you I wouldn't have," Alan's voice broke into her thoughts. "You know I love you. We like the same things, we're both quiet, we have the kids . . . I know you don't mind if I spend half my life with cows." He grinned.

"You're generous and loving, Jan, just as you were at twenty-one, though you didn't let me see yourself till Viv had gone. When you did, I liked what I saw. I still do."

It was the longest speech he had ever made. No doubt, Janet thought, it would have to last for the remainder of their life together.

Slowly, she held out her hand, roughened with work, and Alan took it in his.

Looking up she saw his hair receding a little, with strands of grey, saw his face, weather-beaten from so many winters on the farm.

"I was amazed when I saw Vivian tonight," he was saying. "I would never have dreamed a woman could change so much . . ."

* **THE END** *

BETWEEN OURSELVES

WRITING ON THE WALL!

When we moved into another house, we decided to decorate the living-room.

When we stripped the wall-paper off one wall we found this message from the previous owners.

"We hope you enjoy decorating the room as much as we did, but mind the nasty crack over the window and don't forget to stop for a cup of tea. Good luck!"

This amused us so much that we have left a message under our new wallpaper, which we hope will give someone else a laugh in a few years time!

A SHOCKING HABIT!

Jane, a fashion-conscious five-year-old, was met from school by her grandma.

"Could you make a new dress for my teacher, Nan?" Jane asked. "She's so old fashioned and wears the same old long black thing every day. Make her something short, in nice bright pink."

Jane goes to a convent school!

A STICKY END!

At the cinema one night, my boyfriend bought me an ice-cream. But when I dug the plastic spoon into the container, it bent back on itself instead of lifting out some ice-cream.

Suddenly, with a loud plop, all the ice-cream shot up in the air and vanished over the edge of the balcony!

A startled shriek came from below, but thankfully the lights went out just then and hid my red face.

ANXIOUS MOMENT

I never believed that it was possible when I read that someone had "lived through a lifetime of fear in the space of a few minutes."

That was until the day my fourth child was born.

My first three were boys and when I heard the words "It's a lovely little girl," I was ecstatic.

Then came a dreadful silence instead of the expected yell.

It was only a few moments before my daughter expressed her opinion of the world, but I truly lived through a lifetime of fear as I waited to hear that cry, which must be the most glorious sound on earth.

TIME'S UP!

I wonder why so many people get a clock or a watch when they retire.

I never want to see the time again when I stop work!

All through your schooldays, the clock is your enemy, then when you go to work you always have to keep an eye on the time.

To me, the ideal present would be a lovely travelling case and a cheque, to have a long carefree holiday!

All Things Nice . . .

And that, as any father will tell you, is what little girls are made of . . .

WHEN Paul proposed to Ginny, he had been ready to forgive her all her excesses — raspberry-pink lipstick, tutti-frutti ice cream and foreign films.

"We'll have children," Ginny had declared. "Lots."

"Two for a start, anyway," Paul had promised.

And he'd vowed to himself their children would grow up to accept the world with their eyes wide open. Apart from seeing them safely through each day, parents also had the responsibility of making certain their children met life squarely, without blinkers. His father had seen to it he had.

Now, 11 years later, Paul lounged in his armchair, drink in hand, and wondered why things hadn't worked out as he'd intended.

Hearing Ginny call good night to the girls upstairs, he knew the first part of the bargain had been kept. It was the second part that continued to elude him. Each day he lost a little more ground. Only last week he'd been badgered into buying two transistor radios, complete with earphones.

Paul sighed. Not a leaf stirred in the old elms along the drive. They lived in an old farmhouse, four miles from the college where he worked, that Ginny had fallen in love with the minute she saw it. Good thing, too, since his associate professor's salary couldn't cover much else.

"It's perfect for raising children," she'd crowed. It didn't matter that the plumbing belonged in the Stone Age, or the mice often ate better than they did.

Ginny collapsed in the chair beside him — long legged, much given to pullovers and stretch pants. "I'm exhausted. How about some coffee?"

"Think I'll stick to this, thanks." He grinned. "By the way, I found your eldest going through the kitchen drawers a while ago — looking for something to go digging with. Says she's hunting flying pterodactyl fossils in the morning, over at the Bryson farm. They're digging another septic tank."

His wife sighed. "Cass is the only ten-year-old I know who'd rather go hunting fossils than see a pop group."

Paul, who had only the vaguest notion about pop groups, shrugged his shoulders. "Cassie knows how to cope."

His wife gave him a pitying look. "You ought to see her on a school morning when I haven't ironed the one special blouse she's simply got to have. Children don't cope, pet."

"Why not? I did." It was his favourite theme. The trouble was, nobody listened. What could you expect of a house full of women? "I used to get up at four in the morning to deliver papers, and after school I swept out Smith's butcher's shop."

"Poor darling." The shadows of the old poplar sifted over her face. "Gail wants a violin for her birthday."

Paul smiled fondly. "Next week it'll be butterflies." ►p50

Complete Story by
LOIS STUART EWEN

◀p48
He loved his youngest with a kind of baffled wonderment. Gail was a collector of things. Shells and stones and tropical fish, of which the darting golden fantails (Winkie and Blinkie, a variation on the old nursery rhyme) were her favourites.

Sometimes his daughter seemed as elusive to him as the fish. For ever dreaming, listening to things he could not hear, slipping away to her secret world on the hill behind the house.

Ginny helped herself to some crisps. "No, I'm serious. She was up in her room all morning in front of the mirror — pretending to play. It's not the first time."

PAUL straightened slowly. Shells and stones were one thing. A violin was quite another.

"She's tone deaf," he protested.

It was true. She tried all the time, involved versions of school songs and stuff she heard on the radio. But his lovely dreamer had no voice at all. Gail sang in a monotone — blissfully unaware.

Ginny sighed. "I haven't the heart to tell her."

"You've got to be honest with them. That's half the trouble with the world today — over-indulgence. Violins. Ten-thousand-pound racing cars. We're raising a generation of misfits."

Ginny helped herself to more crisps. "There are second-hand violins, Paul. Even ones for renting."

"For Pete's sake, Gin. The roof needs patching, rates are going up, and you talk about violins."

She uncurled from the cushions and got up. "Everybody deserves a chance to try."

"What's that supposed to mean? I'm an ogre who denies his own children? Besides, suppose they fall on their faces?"

She looked at him thoughtfully. "Why, then I'll be there to pick up the pieces — and that's better than not having tried at all." Her stare was pointed. "If you're so keen on this truth business, why don't you tell her yourself?" The door banged.

Paul followed her, sighing. He was a soft-hearted idiot when it came to his youngest, and Ginny knew it.

He stood in Gail's doorway, gazing down at the dark hair fanning over the pillow. Her slender arms were wrapped around Anne-Marie, the doll of the moment. Twenty-five years ago people hadn't gone around talking about permissiveness and repressions. You told a child he couldn't have something, and that was that.

The fantails shimmered in their small tank on top of Gail's dresser. Didn't they ever sleep, he wondered, gliding about in their silent, watery world. Turning away, he was suddenly assailed by a vision of his daughter floating across a stage as big as the Albert Hall, Stradivarius in hand . . .

All right. He would have a talk with her in the morning before this violin business got out of hand.

PAUL was up early next morning. At the university, he was to supervise an English exam, though his own field happened to be qualitative analysis. He'd let himself get trapped into giving up a perfectly good Wednesday morning to help out a friend. What he'd planned to do was assemble some notes on waste-water management for a pamphlet he was working on.

"Call Gail for breakfast, will you, darling?" Ginny asked him. "She's up on the hill."

He decided the walk would do him good. "Gail's Hill," they called it. For some reason, nobody else went up there.

When he reached the top, puffing more than he cared to admit, he found his daughter standing with her back to him in a small clearing partially screened by bushes. Far off, he could make out the Bryson farm.

But the clearing was a private world. And Gail was going through a silent pantomime with two sticks. He didn't need a programme to tell him it was girl, playing violin.

He retreated beyond the screen of bushes. Then he cleared his throat.

"Time for breakfast," he called out to her.

When his daughter emerged from the clearing, her hands were empty.

"What's this your mother tells me about your wanting a violin for your birthday?" he asked as they walked down the hill.

Gail pushed hair out of her eyes, face shining. "Oh, Daddy, can I — can I, please?"

"May . . ." he corrected, feeling helpless in the face of all that longing.

"It doesn't have to be a good one, Daddy. Not at first." And then like a young colt running on the wind, she started down the path ahead of him, hair streaming. "Not until I'm . . ." the words tailed thinly ". . . accomplished!"

"I'll remember that," he-of-little-resolve murmured.

Paul was still blaming himself for dodging the issue when he walked into the staff lounge for a quick smoke before the exam. A fellow associate professor, who indulged in chamber music on the side, sank into the nearest chair.

"Tell me something, Al," Paul said. "If a person's tone deaf, can he ever learn to play an instrument? A violin, say?"

"Depends. Oh, he might — in a technical sense. But he'd never be able to hear the music. There's a difference, you know."

Paul got to his feet heavily. The central heating was making his head throb. "Well, 'Into the jaws of death, Into the mouth of hell . . .' "

Fifteen minutes into the exam, he caught a boy cribbing answers, one of his own students from last year. Machinery had been set up to handle such situations, but he ignored it. In cold fury, he banished the offender to his office, then refused to listen to the sorry tale afterwards.

"You cheated — it's as simple as that."

GINNY was preparing lunch when he got home. His head ached wildly by this time.

"Take a couple of headache pills," Ginny advised sympathetically.

He swallowed two in a glass of water. "Where is everybody?"

"Cass is sulking in the shed. Mr Bryson refused to let her within fifty feet of the vital digs." She gave him a significant look. "Gail's been playing lady virtuoso all morning." ►p54

Beware Of The CAT

ARE you sitting comfortably? You are? Then I'll begin . . .

Friends, humans and canines, lend me your ears! I come not to perch in this horrible old speaker's rostrum, but to plead a cause that is close to my heart.

I speak of me.

I am not at all happy with the state of comfort in which I am kept. I am not content with the quality of food which I am fed. I am not at all satisfied with the world in which I live.

I am not greedy or demanding, but clearly some changes will have to be made.

To begin with, I feel it should be more clearly understood that in keeping you humans as our pets, we cats are not prepared to allow you to assert yourselves in any aggressive and arrogant manner.

It's a cat's world. And if you would only remember that, it would be a better world for all of us.

There's No Place Like Home . . .

A YOUNG friend is learning the truth of that the hard way!

For many months, she has been telling her mother, and anyone else who would listen, that she must, she simply must, get away from home.

She wants her freedom, she says. But when asked what exactly this "freedom" will give her she has no ready answer.

But evidently "freedom" means a flat of one's own. "Freedom" means a kitchen of one's own. "Freedom" means a place where no parents are around.

The fact that "freedom" will mean paying a substantial whack off her wages in rent and other bills seems to mean little. Neither does the fact that "freedom" will only become possible if understanding parents part with bed linen, crockery, and a few items of furniture.

Do I sound too critical? I don't mean to be . . . but I find it hard to understand the present trend among young people to shout loudly of "freedom" and "independence" — when all the time they are dependent on the love and generosity of parents.

The young lady concerned has been to see many flats. But she has liked none. Always there are snags.

The plain truth is, of course, that none offer the comfort and security of her home. Even flats of a good standard, which she was invited to share with other girls of her own age, failed to appeal to her.

In these cases, it seemed that company of her own age had as many drawbacks as the company of her parents!

I feel sorry for her. It must be very frustrating to be young and restless — and yet to feel so uncertain of what step to take.

I'm told that many parents face the same problem as my friends with their daughter. I'd be interested to hear how it all works out!

Do they really leave home — and find a settled future on their own? Or do they leave — only to come home more appreciative of all that they have had in the past?

Chairs are constructed, beds are made, carpets are designed, and fires are laid — all for the single purpose of making a cat's life cosy and comfortable. There are times, though I am the last to be greedy or demanding, when it is clear that some of you forget this, and some even aspire to treatment as equals!

You people must learn to be content with your lot in life. You are all born to serve us. To go shopping for the delicious food that others of you labour to produce. Your destiny, dear humans, lies not in your stars but in the earning of money that produces milk and fish and liver.

The ancient Pharaohs were wonderful people. Intelligent people. Wise, deep-thinking people. And they, of course. worshipped cats.

My patience, you know, is not inexhaustible. I *can* be roused to great wrath. So I feel compelled to give you solemn warning. Unless all of you develop a new and more respectful attitude towards us cats, I will not be held responsible for the dreadful things that might afflict you humans.

Such as mice in the bedroom . . . birds on the seedbeds . . . a wailing and a caterwauling throughout the hours of early morning . . . to name but a few.

So change while there is yet time! And all shall be well with you and yours!

And though I am not greedy or demanding, I'll have seven pounds of fish and a pint of milk . . . just for starters.

◀p51

"Oh, great." Paul heaved a long sigh. He didn't need this type of news.

That night, sitting on the sofa, he nursed a strong dose of self-righteousness. He was in the doghouse again. Dark allusions had been made to a garden fence he'd neglected to fix, and to the TV which hadn't worked for a week.

Beside him, Ginny finally stirred and scratched an ankle. "I went over with the egg money this morning. Mrs Bryson said she'd let us have Ted's old violin for twenty pounds. Her sister lives in town," Ginny went on. "She only charges two pounds an hour for beginners. Oh, Paul," she appealed, "twenty pounds. What can we lose?"

"Twenty pounds, for a start." He straightened slowly. "Gin, you're serious, aren't you?"

"I think she needs a chance to try."

"You've said that already. For Pete's sake, love — face facts. She's never going to be a child prodigy."

"Who wants a child prodigy? All I'm saying is, if she wants to mess around with a violin, what harm can it do?"

"Gail wouldn't know middle C from a hole in the ground."

"Is that so important?" She looked into his face. "All right, Paul. You've made your point. I won't bring it up again."

Was she serious? She was. He got to his feet. "I'll talk to her in the morning. Is that what you want?"

Ginny didn't answer.

Paul sighed. "I think I'll go up. Coming?"

"I just want to sit here a bit longer, thank you."

He was just getting into bed when she came into the room.

"Your eldest woke up a minute ago," he told her. "She says she's going back to the archaeological digs. I told her she stands a fat chance of moving a bloke like Bryson."

Ginny got her dressing-gown and slippers out of the wardrobe.

"Given the proper motivation, people have moved mountains," she said cryptically.

PAUL had no chance to take Gail aside next morning before he drove off to collect the exam papers he'd been too tired to tackle the day before. When he got back, instead of working on the water-management notes he'd planned, he risked pneumonia clearing what must have amounted to a quarter acre of weeds Ginny had been after him to clear.

"It doesn't have to be done on the coldest day of the year," she reminded him tartly, bringing him out a cup of coffee. "It'll still be here in the morning."

If he'd had any strength of purpose at all, he would have refused the drink, too. But the fact was, he might have frozen on the spot without it.

"I've come this far," he growled, "I'm going to finish the thing."

She gazed at him without comment, then went back to the house. He watched her, the little damp wisps straggling down the nape of her neck. Nice neck — for a stubborn female.

That night he played baby-sitter while Ginny went to one of those bridge affairs the staff wives were always putting on. Standing at the foot of Gail's bed, he listened to her prayers.

". . . and please, God, let my violin be here for my birthday. Anne-Marie wants me to play *Scarlet Ribbons.* Amen."

He stared down at the soft curve of cheek, the clasped doll.

"About the violin, love," he began. "There are some things a person has to . . . adjust to in life. Like not being able to dance like Margot Fonteyn. Or write a book. Or play the violin. A hundred different things we look back on later as not having been important."

"But it is important, Daddy."

"Yes, it is — now. But later . . ."

Her smile was meant to comfort him. "Never mind, Daddy. I can play it. You'll see."

His throat squeezed tight. All that bright longing. All that innocence and trust. He wanted her to meet life on even terms, her eyes clear . . .

"Why, sweetheart?" he asked softly. "Why do you want to play it?"

She turned to the window and the moon riding the windless old elms. There it was again, that air of listening to something out there in the dark. Something he could not hear.

"Because it's so — so — pretty," she finished.

Don't, he wanted to tell her. Go back to your shells and stones. But he leaned down and kissed her instead. "Good night, love."

Cass sat cross-legged on the bed when he went in to her. She had something rusty and begrimed in her hands which she examined closely. "I found it this afternoon. Mr Bryson let me sift through the stuff he's already dug.

Score one for Cass. "Early Bronze Age perhaps?"

Her brows pursed critically. "Maybe it's an old flintlock used in the Civil War."

"Put it away, love. We'll clean it up in the morning and see what we've got."

AT his desk, Paul tried to concentrate on the exam papers. His thoughts revolved in muddy circles. Rates. The face of the cheating student. Gail. Why did he let her go on building hopes?

He pushed out of his chair and went into the dark kitchen to make coffee. Reaching for the switch, he thought he saw a light in the shed. But when he looked again to make sure, he was mistaken.

The coffee was bitter, the cigarettes stale by the time he called it quits. The exam papers were still unfinished, but he didn't care. They'd still be there in the morning. He'd wait up for Ginny, hear about how the associate professor's wife had no-trumped again.

Stepping out on to the porch, he stretched cramped muscles, staring into the heavens. A kind of icy stillness hung in the air. And this time when he looked, sure enough, there was a light in the shed.

Cassie was hunched on a stool under the naked bulb. She was scraping at the relic with a file. She didn't even have the grace to look shamefaced.

"Well," he said, "I see you didn't take my advice."

"I had to find out, Daddy."

"And?"

"Well, it isn't a flintlock, for one thing." Cass sighed. ▶p58

DOUBLE TROUBLE

THE first time I ever saw him, I remember thinking clearly what a smashing good-looker he was.

Why, I thought in a flash of inspiration, he looks almost as beautiful as me!

That shows you how fair minded I am. For to be truthful, there's nobody as breathtakingly handsome as me. Or so downright modest, to boot!

Having an identical twin around ought to have its advantages. I can't think of any, but I feel there ought to be some . . . just to outweigh the disadvantages.

To start with, he eats far too much. And he eats far too fast. I really have to bolt my food down at a shocking rate in order to help him finish off his.

Our dog basket was never meant for two. Now I don't mind sharing: I'm as reasonable as anyone has a right to expect. But can I help it if I tend to lie on his face or push him off our blanket when I'm fast asleep?

Another thing — I know he's delicate. Well, I don't really know, but it's the only possible explanation for the idiotic way he acts at times. And so, you see, I have to protect him from too much petting and caressing. That's why I always volunteer for a double dose of adulation from visitors . . . and anybody who says anything different is a liar.

There are many other disadvantages, but you haven't got the time and I haven't got the energy to go over them all. Besides, I'm not one to complain, you know.

Let me just say this — I love the guy. I love him in a great unselfish way . . . so much so, that if anybody wanted to take him away, I wouldn't stop them. I wouldn't even think of stopping them . . .

A Most Serious Business . . .

SHE stood on the busy pavement, heedless of the people jostling past her. Slowly and calmly, she surveyed the contents of the window of the expensive fashion salon.

Critically she eyed a dream of a cocktail dress, and her nose wrinkled in open disapproval. She merely glanced at the "simple little black dress" (one of these which cost a small fortune) as she moved on to a rather sophisticated trouser suit in bright flame, with lashings of gilt trimmings at the collar and cuffs, all finished off by a heavy gilt chain belt.

Her face brightened with clear approval. As she noted the gilt open-work sandals, she smiled. This, clearly, was for her!

Hands behind her back, she rocked to and fro, gazing admiringly at the trouser suit. Such colour, such glitter!

Nothing else in the window appealed. She stood, lost in her day-dreams of glamour, until suddenly a woman darted out of the shop, grabbed her by the arm, and proceeded to give her a good telling-off for wandering out of the shop.

Obediently — but with a last glance at the trouser suit — the little girl went back into the shop — with her mother!

◀p55
"Here, let me have it." He took the file and scraped carefully, then wiped off as much of the dirt and rust as he could with his handkerchief.
"No," he said finally, "it isn't. I'll tell you what it is, though. It's the handle from an old coffee-grinder."
Cass didn't say anything for a minute. And then she heaved a philosophic sigh. "Could we grind coffee with it?"
"Not the way it is. Tell you what, though. If you like, we'll see if there's an old grinder around to sell. How does that sound?"
She shook her head politely. "Thanks, Daddy, but I think I'll go on digging. Mr Bryson says if I keep out of the way it's OK."
He stared at her with admiration. Cass might stub her toe now and then, but she'd never lose sight of the main road.
"Right," he said. "But for now — bed, young lady, or you'll never be able to tell a flying pterodactyl from one that does the Australian crawl."
"Oh, Daddy."
Ginny came home at midnight. She went straight to bed without telling him about the associate history professor's wife.

PAUL had been lying in bed for an hour when he awakened from a restless doze. Had someone called out? He got up cautiously so as not to wake Ginny.
Cass lay on her back with her mouth open, a hand on her book — the neolithic division of archaeology, he noted with a smile, slipping it free. Would she ever tire of learning, he wondered.
At Gail's door, he stopped. She sat bolt upright. And in the murky half gloom, Winkie and Blinkie swished quietly.
"Anne-Marie . . ." she mumbled thickly.
For a moment the light from the window played tricks on him. It seemed that his daughter was a slender sea nymph rising from dark waters. If he didn't reach out for her quickly, she would be snatched from him on the incoming tide.
"Daddy — has it come?"
The blasted violin again. "We'll talk about it tomorrow."
Her eyes suddenly cleared. "It's the money, isn't it? I heard you and Mummy talking about rates. Daddy, please tell me."
He sat down on the bed, dismayed, the book still in his hand. Children had a way of catching you unawares.
He took her hand. "I didn't say I didn't want you to have it, love," he said slowly. "Only sometimes people want something and — they're disappointed later. It doesn't always turn out the way they expect."
She slipped her hand out of his and stared at the elms and high, thin clouds beyond the window — again the listening. "I've been thinking about what it looks like, Daddy. It's like the leaves. And the rain. And — and — the sound of the wind when it blows on the hill."
He didn't know if it was the coffee and the cigarettes, and the fact that it was two o'clock in the morning and he was bone tired, but suddenly his eyes stung.
"Daddy . . . ?" Gail stared at the tank of slowly-swimming fish. "If I sold Winkie and Blinkie to the man at the pet shop, would I have enough to buy the violin?"

The neolithic division of archaeology slipped from his lap. He bent to get it, grateful he didn't have to look at his daughter's face.

"You know that sound, Daddy?" she went on. "The one I was telling you about? Sometimes I think maybe I can't. But I want to. I want to try to play that sound, Daddy."

His fingers traced the cover of Cass's book, the words that astounded him each time he heard them from his daughter's lips. From the day Cass was born they had known she would be one of the seekers. Solemn, intent on every bug, leaf and clod of earth.

He thought of the flintlock which had turned out to be not very much, after all. He thought of the philosophic shrug. And he knew that Cass didn't need him, maybe she never would.

Gail plucked at his sleeve. "Will you take me to the pet shop, Daddy?"

Wonderingly, he searched her face. Cass didn't need him, but what of the dreamer? Hadn't he always thought he'd known what was best for her — the truth, clear eyed and simple?

"Daddy?"

HE reached out and smoothed back the soft hair. All kinds of drums rolled for his daughter, he knew now. Drums no-one else could hear. Ginny had known. Known that it wasn't the importance of conquering the unconquerable, but only the importance of trying that really mattered.

Carefully, he laid Cass's book on the table and cleared his throat.

"I have a better idea," he said. "Tomorrow after breakfast we'll walk over to Mrs Bryson's. I think if we ask her politely she might let you see her violin."

Gail's eyes widened. "A real one?"

He nodded. "She might even let you earn part of the money to buy it yourself. You could help her collect the eggs."

"Oh, Daddy," she breathed, "do you think we could?"

He kissed her and rose. "Now go back to sleep. It's late, and your old dad's tired."

Ginny met him outside in the hall. How long had she been standing there? She put her arms around him and leaned her head against his chest.

"Thank you," she murmured against him.

He freed himself gently. "Gin, it wasn't the money."

"You idiot. Did you think you were fooling anybody?"

"You can call that old biddy and tell her we're interested in buying the blasted thing."

"I already have."

He stared at his wife's bemused face. He didn't know whether to shake her or laugh. "Oh, you have, have you?" And he kissed her instead. "That's what I get for marrying a stubborn, extravagant woman."

And together they went back to their room.

*** THE END ***

It was quite a reunion when Piggy Morgan met his old flame Pudding Davies . . . whom he hadn't seen since they were both fifteen years old!

DON'T I KNOW YOU?

Complete Story by
BETTY SUTTON

WHEN Edna Davies first walked into the Llynmair Garage she could find nobody about at all. Then a movement caught her eye. She crossed to the far corner, her regulation black oxfords making no noise on the concrete.

Two green, overalled legs protruded from between the rear wheels of a car.

Edna nudged one leg with the toe of her shoe.

"Excuse me," she said. "I want to speak to Mr Rupert Morgan. Can you tell me where I might find him?"

The legs emerged farther, followed by a broad chest and eventually a harassed-looking face smudged with oil.

"I'm Rupert Morgan."

"And I'm Miss Davies. I wrote you. Three times. My car is practically new, Mr Morgan. It shouldn't be getting rusty already."

The man sat up and regarded her. " 'Under mass production, occasional faults slip through the fine mesh of our quality control,' " he quoted.

"Dear me!" exclaimed Edna. "You'll have to do better than that."

He looked annoyed. Also, he winced as he got up and she glanced at the cold concrete floor.

Probably sciatica, she thought, annoyed that her nursing instinct should produce such a sneaky thought at a time when she wanted to be tough.

"Will you come into the office?"

Edna guessed he felt happier under the car, and when she reached his office it was easy to see why.

The "In" basket was piled with correspondence, technical magazines and brochures tumbled in untidy heaps over the two desks. Both waste paper baskets were full of rags and tissues, liberally smeared with oil, and with empty cartons and bags from the nearby bakery.

No proper meals, registered Edna's trained mind.

"Haven't you got a secretary?" she asked, as he began ineffectively looking for her letters.

"They never stay," he said, as though it wasn't his fault. He opened a couple of the drawers of the metal filing cabinet and peered unhappily at the dusty files.

The untidiness made Edna fidgety.

"I can explain quite easily," she said briskly. "The exhaust pipe is rusty, already. And I haven't had the car three months."

"Oh, yes of *course!*" he exclaimed. "Your letters are in the *Complaints* file! I just haven't got round to dealing with them yet."

He picked up a bulging blue envelope file and displayed it happily. One of her letters was on top.

"And how do you propose to deal with them?" she asked. "With your fine mesh of quality control?"

"This particular model is extremely reliable," he told her. "I have one myself. I've done thirty thousand miles without a speck of rust. I expect you're a potterer."

"I beg your pardon?" Edna exclaimed.

"You potter about doing short journeys, never giving the exhaust a chance to dry out. And then you wonder why it rusts up."

"Are you suggesting the car is designed only for long distance rally drivers?" she demanded.

"No, merely that you might be better suited with a bicycle," he said, quite unforgivably.

Edna was furious. "And you are obviously better suited as a mechanic," she snapped. "Whoever gave you the job of managing this garage wants his head examining."

"Naturally we'll replace the exhaust under the guarantee," Rupert Morgan said coldly. "Leave your car on the forecourt and it will be ready by the weekend."

"I'm afraid I can't spare that much time. I'm too busy *pottering about.* I'll bring it in on Saturday morning and I shall need it Monday morning, nine o'clock sharp."

She turned and stalked away, climbed into her car, revved the engine violently and swept out of the Llynmair Garage.

Any ideas of giving Rupert Morgan a clue to jolt his memory had gone completely overboard. She didn't care if she never saw him again. Besides, he hadn't recognised her. He'd probably forgotten Edna Davies ever existed.

HOWEVER, it wasn't easy to get away from Rupert Morgan. By Thursday morning of her first week in the village, Edna counted at least six patients who had praised him to the skies.

Old Mrs Clayton, in the middle of being bed-bathed, remarked on the miraculous way young Mr Morgan had fixed her wheel-chair. Alex Foster, who had torn his arm while apple scrumping, told her that Mr Morgan let him help in the garage on Saturday mornings. Gave him a couple of pounds too. He was smashing, was Mr Morgan.

Mrs Benson, whose baby girl needed a booster jab against tetanus, couldn't understand why that nice Mr Morgan had never married. Too busy building up the business, she supposed. Such a nice fellow too. So obliging. He was sure to make a success of the garage.

Edna sniffed and said she wondered. Old Grandad Hughes at the Red Dragon used Rupert Morgan's taxi service. So rcasonablc. So reliable. His two grandsons had both bought their motor bikes at the Llynmair Garage and never had a minute's trouble with them. It seemed the entire village approved of Rupert Morgan.

AT ten past one that Thursday, in the middle of her lunch, Edna had a call from Dr Mansfield to ask if she could come straightaway to Heston Cottage. She hopped into her car, making a face at the Llynmair Garage as she passed.

At Heston Cottage the first Williams baby was making short work of his arrival in the world. Edna took over and Dr Mansfield departed.

"I shall call him Rupert," Brenda Williams said sleepily as Edna tucked her into the re-made bed. "If that young Mr Morgan hadn't brought mc homc double-quick I'd have had the baby in the greengrocer's all among the fruit and veg. I'd never have heard the end of it."

Edna finished attending to Rupert Williams, who seemed satisfied at having made a safe landing and had gone straight to sleep. She stroked the downy hair with a tender forefinger, checked that the mother was sleeping, too, and went downstairs.

She had just tidied up and made a cup of tea when there was a knock on the back door of the cottage.

It was Rupert. She was gratified to find him looking a bit sheepish.

"Come to see your prospective godson?" she asked.

"Dr Mansfield told me the baby was OK," he said. "I've really come to see you. I wanted to apologise for that remark about pottering. I'd no idea until Dr Mansfield told me, that you had taken over from old Smithy as district nurse."

Edna regarded him coolly. "Sit down and have a cup of tea," she suggested. "You've a bit more apologising than that to do."

She noticed the wince as he sat on the hard chair.

"First, while I remember," she said, unzipping her bag. She found a tube and handed it to him. "Use this. Rub night and morning and get into the habit of lying on a rug, not directly on a concrete floor. That way you may avoid hobbling about like an old man before your time."

He took the ointment without speaking, smelt at it and made a face. Then he took a long, long look at her.

Edna busied herself with the tea cosy.

"I thought there was something about you the other day," he said, half to himself. "But you've changed past belief — you're so slim, and your hair . . ." He laughed suddenly. "You're Pudding Davies!"

"And you're Piggy Morgan," she said.

THEY looked at each other over the table and 15 years fell away. They were once more two rather plump children who had just shared an enormous picnic by the shores of Lake Llynmair.►p65

BEWARE OF THE CATS

WE don't really understand why you people like to sit at *tables* when you eat. It seems to us an awful lot of unnecessary trouble for what is, after all, a simple operation of stuffing oneself with goodies.

But, being broad minded, we must say we have no objection to tables being set for meals. (For one thing, it does advertise the fact that food is about to be available.)

Take this floor, for example. There we were, padding around rather dolefully, wondering whether to scare the living daylights out of the birds in the garden, or to scare the living daylights out of ourselves by playing tag with the Alsatian next door.

And we saw this milk. And we saw our opportunity.

We have long thought that whoever said, "Drinkapintaday" was a genius. And here we are, doing a lap-lap in his honour.

Some of you might well consider what we're doing as an act of thieving. Oh well, everyone to her opinion. But isn't there something in the Good Book about helping those who help themselves?

After all, we would like to point out that cats can't go on the National Welfare for a little extra with which to buy the good things of life . . . and neither can we get supplies of milk prescribed on the NHS — even when we are feeling proper poorly.

We need our milk. It's the only thing which keeps up our strength to enable us to go in search of milk with which to keep up our strength — well, you get the idea, don't you?

One small complaint — there's no cream in this milk . . .

◀p63

"Do you remember," he asked her, "how the twins didn't turn up and we ate four pork pies?"

"And all the sandwiches," she said.

"Both bottles of lemonade."

"And two packets of biscuits."

They laughed helplessly and then he demanded: "Did you know who I was — the other day, when you came into my garage? I suppose I've changed too."

To herself she admitted that he had. Only her feelings were unchanged. She had been in love with that podgy schoolboy and she was attracted to the tall, broad-shouldered man he had become.

Perhaps she would never have applied for Smithy's job if Rupert hadn't given his garage the name of their picnic lake, if she hadn't felt sure he remembered, too. And perhaps even now she was placing far too much importance on a childhood memory.

Aloud she said, "Yes, you've changed. You didn't have sciatica then."

He laughed again, stood up, and winced.

"Have you ever been back to Llynmair?" he asked.

She shook her head. "Soon afterwards I had to leave the village to start my training. Somehow I never went back."

"I went away too," he said. "It's odd, isn't it? You know, we ought to have another picnic there — sometime when we're not too busy. Are you — usually — pretty busy?"

"Well — yes — usually," said Edna. She got up and took their cups to the sink.

"Well," he said. "We must do it sometime, anyway."

He insisted on drying the few dishes for her, and then she watched him walk down the path to the gate. Suddenly, he turned and came back. Edna opened the window.

"Could you manage Saturday afternoon?" he asked.

"Yes, I think so. If you really want to go . . ."

"I do," he said. "I'll bring the meat pies and the drinks."

"All right," she said. "I'll bring sandwiches and biscuits . . ."

*** THE END ***

AT LAST — A CURE!

During the twenty-five years of our marriage, I have often been kept awake by my husband's snores. So when we were given a tape recorder, the first thing I did was to tape my husband one night. I played it back to him next day.

He was appalled at the noise. "Turn it off," he begged, but I replied that as I had listened to it for twenty-five years he could just suffer it for ten mintues.

The amazing thing is he hasn't snored so loudly since!

It was end-of-term day at school. The kind of day when anything could happen . . .

TEACHERS are funny, Tim thought.

There they were, Dave Merrow and he, filling the inkwells in the little back room of Miss Jones' classroom, just as they had been doing every Thursday afternoon all the term. And yet everybody knew the next school day would be the last one, and nobody would be needing any ink for the whole six weeks of the summer holiday.

Teachers always made you do the same old thing in the same old way. ►p68

Complete Story by EILEEN ELIAS

OF
MICE
AND
MEN

◀p66
David and he rather enjoyed the job of being ink monitors. At least it got them out of dictation on Thursday afternoons, and they were neither of them much good at dictation. Still, with coaching from Miss Jones, they'd managed to win the two special scholarships given to boys between nine and ten for the junior school at Bradhurst. They would be starting there next term.

"Last day tomorrow, Tim," Dave said cheerfully, tipping the big, brown teapot with the long spout that was used for filling inkwells.

Theirs was one of the classes where inkwells were still preferred to ballpoint pens. That was Miss Jones again. "Nobody can learn to write without learning how to use a nib," she had insisted.

So they all used pens, and Dave and Tim liked the job of cleaning the inkwells and pouring out the blue-black liquid that dripped in satisfying blobs all over the tin tray that held the 30 little china pots.

"It'll be good at Bradhurst," Tim said, holding the tray steady while Dave poured. A blob fell on to Tim's fingers, and he looked about for the ink rag. When he didn't find it, he fished for his handkerchief in a pocket. Since he didn't find that either, Dave lent him his.

"We'll be wearing black blazers," Tim went on, handing back the inky handkerchief. "And going to school by train instead of on our bikes."

Dave nodded and filled six more inkwells before he spoke.

"What're you going to give Miss Jones?" he said at last.

"Miss Jones?" said Tim, "Why do I have to give Miss Jones anything?"

Dave looked up.

"My dad says it was Miss Jones who got us both into Bradhurst. So he's promised me a bunch of his best roses to take tomorrow, as it's the last day. Sort of thank-you, see?"

TIM considered. This was something new to him. He hadn't given a thought to any present for Miss Jones. Nobody at home had mentioned it either. He hadn't any roses in his garden, only lettuces. And he'd no money to go and buy anything.

All the same, Tim didn't like the idea of being left out of things. He liked Miss Jones; next to Mr Patrick, who took woodwork and Boys' Games, he liked her best of all. If anybody was giving her presents, Tim didn't want to be missed out.

"If I give Miss Jones anything," Tim said grandly, "it'll be a much nicer present than roses! Who wants roses, anyway?"

Dave looked annoyed. "What're you going to give her then?"

Tim had no idea, but he knew he had to think of something quick.

Dave was silent a moment, then he grinned wickedly. "Tell you one thing you wouldn't give her."

"What, then?"

"Your Benjy."

"Bet I would," Tim said.

"Bet you'd never."

"All right," Tim announced. "You wait and see."

Dave looked at him with an unbelieving stare, and then for the first time Tim realised the enormity of what he'd said.

He'd had Benjy nearly three months now, and he liked him better than anything in the world. He wasn't just an ordinary black or white mouse. No. Benjy's fur was a delicate brown and white, the colour of hen's feathers.

Tim had bought him in the market one Saturday when he was only as big as Tim's own fingernail, and all this time he had watched him grow.

Benjy had a delicious trick of running up inside Tim's sleeve when he took him in his hand; it gave a tingly feeling all the way up Tim's arm. Little mouse's feet running. Nobody but Tim knew that feeling.

He had told Mr Patrick about Benjy and Mr Patrick had helped him make a cage in the woodwork class. Tim had bought a little wheel for Benjy to push round, and made a bridge up to his sleeping quarters.

It wasn't fair, thought Tim; Dave knew how much he liked Benjy. Hadn't they taken turns with him on the days he came to school in Tim's pocket, Dave having him all through English and Arithmetic, and Tim in Geography and Religious Instruction?

And now, all in a moment, just because of one stupid dare, Benjy was to go.

"P'raps she doesn't like mice," Tim suggested. "Lots of ladies don't. My mum didn't at first."

" 'Course she likes 'em," scoffed Dave. "You're only saying that to get out of it."

It was no good. Tim turned back to the inkwells.

"All right," he said. "Tomorrow Miss Jones gets Benjy. And she'll like him a lot better than she'll like your dad's old roses, see?"

After all, he could always buy another mouse.

IT wasn't till he had got his bicycle out of the shed and was pedalling back over the railway bridge that the full impact struck him. Buy another? Of course he couldn't. What other mouse would ever be just like Benjy?

He reached home, pushed open the gate and led his bike through into the yard. He propped it against the wall and made for the garden shed.

Inside, he reached up and took down Benjy's cage from its place amongst dusty flowerpots on the shelf. Carefully he slid open the top.

At once Benjy came to nibble at Tim's finger. Then he ran deftly on to his hand and sat there, trembling delicately. His nose twitched, his tiny bright eyes were alert. Next moment he was running up inside Tim's sleeve.

Tim laughed, rescued him, and held him in his hand again, stroking the soft brown and white back. Then he remembered.

"I can't, Benjy," Tim whispered, close against his fur. And then he thought of Dave. Nobody at school ever refused a dare.

Tim couldn't eat his breakfast next morning. He always had bacon and egg for breakfast on schooldays; there was bacon and egg as usual today, but he left it untouched.

Oddly, his mother didn't make her usual fuss.

"Excitement, Tim, that's what it is," she said. "You just drink this cup of tea. It's your last day and I'm not surprised."

"He's been very lucky to have a teacher like Miss Jones," Dad said over his paper. "Entirely due to that young woman that Tim and David won those scholarships. Come to think of it, we really ought to have given her a little something. Just to say thank-you."

"Too late for that now," his mother said, finding Tim's satchel and gently prodding him towards the door. "Quarter to nine already, and mind how you go on your bike."

Tim didn't tell her about Benjy. The words wouldn't come.

He went out to the shed, opened the cage, and felt Benjy's twitching nose against his hand. He was such a tiny thing to lift out and slip into a trouser pocket; no bigger than a couple of marbles.

Benjy nestled warmly against Tim's side as he cycled, carefully so as not to frighten him, over the railway bridge and round the corner into school.

In the bicycle shed he met Mr Patrick, putting his bike away.

"Hello, Tim," he said.

Tim liked Mr Patrick; he was tall and brown and had a lopsided smile.

"Hello, Mr Patrick," Tim said.

Mr Patrick looked thoughtfully at him. "Let's see," he said. "Miss Jones tells me this'll be your last day here — you and Dave. Glad or sorry?"

"Glad," Tim said automatically; then, catching sight of his kind, friendly face, added, "Well — sort of."

"By the way," Mr Patrick said, leaning on his handlebars. "How's Benjamin?"

Could he have guessed, thought Tim? No, of course not. He started to speak, and then an enormous football swelled up in his throat so that the words got stuck.

Mr Patrick looked at him keenly.

"Nothing wrong with him, I hope?"

"Oh, no." Tim said, finding his voice. He was surprised to hear it croaky. "It's just that I'm not going to have him much longer, I'm giving him to someone — a friend."

Mr Patrick nodded. "I see. A present, eh? Lucky friend."

He gave Tim his lopsided smile, and put a hand momentarily on his shoulder. "Isn't that the bell going? Run along. Can't be late for Miss Jones on your last day."

Tim joined the line in the playground and walked into the cloakroom. On the way he pushed against Dave Merrow, who was holding a bunch of roses wrapped up in fancy paper.

"Bet you haven't brought Benjy," Dave hissed in his ear.

It was Tim's moment of triumph, but it left him cold. He took Benjy out of his pocket for a minute, and Dave gave him an astonished grin.

"Didn't really think you'd do it," he said. Then his grin turned into a beam of admiration. That was one nice thing about Dave, Tim thought. He didn't bear a grudge for long.

ON the last morning, things were different. There were only two lessons, and then the whole school assembled in the hall for end-of-term prayers and to sing *Lord Dismiss Us With Thy Blessing.*

Tim had heard it and sung it so many times that it seemed impossible he would be hearing it no more.

He went into class, got out his books, and settled down to English and

Arithmetic at his desk next to Dave's. Benjy was warm in his pocket, and for once Dave didn't ask to have a turn with him. Tim was glad of that.

The two lessons went by in a kind of fog. Tim could hear Miss Jones talking and watched her doing things on the blackboard with chalk, but he didn't seem able to concentrate. His hand kept straying to Benjy.

At last the bell rang and the class packed up books and filed out into the hall. Miss Jones stood by her desk and smiled. "Nice holidays!" she said.

Dave and Tim were the last to go.

"Well, boys," Miss Jones said. "You won't be coming back next term, will you? I shall have to find two more ink monitors now. Well, I hope you'll be very happy at Bradhurst."

It was Dave's cue. Tim saw him fumbling under his desk for his dad's roses. He walked up to the teacher's table and held them out.

"To say thank-you," he told her. "For getting me the scholarship."

Miss Jones went pink, as she always did when she was pleased and surprised. She took the roses and buried her face in them for a moment.

"They're lovely, David," she said. "It's really very kind of you. And your dad." She held out her hand and shook his. "Thank you again, and best of luck."

Dave went a bright brick-red and ran.

Now there was only Tim left. He took a deep breath and felt in his pocket.

"I've got this for you, Miss Jones," he said, and put Benjy on the table.

Miss Jones said nothing at all. She stepped back a bit, and the words Tim had expected to hear didn't come.

For a moment he wondered why; but then he knew. She was like himself. He could never get a word out when he was terribly pleased.

"His name's Benjy," Tim explained to bridge the gap. "If you haven't got a cage, I'll make you one. Or —" the words came out in a gush — "you can have mine. I — I don't think I'll be keeping any pets any more — not after Benjy."

Still Miss Jones didn't speak, and looking up at her Tim was surprised to see she wasn't pink but white. It was the excitement, of course.

And then he caught sight of Mr Patrick through the glass window in the door. Mr Patrick was just leading his class along the corridor into the hall for prayers, and was looking straight through into Miss Jones' classroom.

He looked at Miss Jones, then he looked at Benjy. Then in two strides he was inside the room. He put one arm round Miss Jones and with the other hand picked up Benjy gently off the table and cupped him in his palm.

"Well," he said to Tim. "So this is your present to a friend. And a very nice one, too. Isn't it, Miss Jones?"

When she didn't answer, he repeated what he had said. "Isn't it, Sue?"

"Oh," Miss Jones was smiling now. "Yes. Yes, of course, Tim. It's a lovely present, and thank you."

She shook hands with Tim, as she had with Dave, and the pain of losing Benjy faded a little. Then the noise outside dropped to a hush, and Tim knew that prayers were beginning. He ran, so as not to be late.

He couldn't help casting a last look through the glass window at Benjy.

Miss Jones and Mr Patrick were still standing there, but Miss Jones was all pink and laughing now, and Tim felt glad he'd made her happy.

Benjy was sitting quietly on Mr Patrick's hand, but Mr Patrick, Tim noticed, wasn't looking at him at all. In fact, neither of them were.

They were looking at each other, and Mr Patrick's arm was still round Miss Jones.

PRAYERS went on for a long time, it seemed to Tim, that morning. Finally he was singing *Lord, Dismiss Us With Thy Blessing* for the last time. Then he and Dave filed out with the others into the cloakroom.

Tim went slowly out into the playground and found his bicycle in the shed. Just as he was pushing it out, he found Mr Patrick at his side.

"Oh, Tim," he said. "Glad I caught you. I wanted to have a word with you. In fact, we both did."

Tim noticed for the first time that Miss Jones was standing close behind.

"Is it about the cage?" he asked. "I'm sorry I didn't bring it with me. I sort of forgot ladies don't have pockets."

"No," Mr Patrick said, "it isn't about the cage. You see, while you've been in prayers, Miss Jones and I have been looking at Benjy — carefully. And we think — that is, Miss Jones thinks — that he's pining a little. Pets do, you know. Specially when they've only been used to one owner."

Tim had nothing to say. He looked at Mr Patrick and then at Miss Jones. He felt cold all over at the thought of Benjy unhappy.

"So we think, Miss Jones and I," Mr Patrick went on, "that it would really be kinder if he went back to you. It's Benjy we're considering. Of course it'll be a sacrifice, but we must put Benjy's happiness first. Mustn't we, Sue?"

A warm feeling began to spread over Tim. Then suddenly the coldness crept back.

"But what about Miss Jones?" He turned to her. "Won't you mind? It's going to be an awful disappointment to you."

"It's the thought that counts, Tim," said Miss Jones, and she was smiling. "It's the nicest goodbye present I ever had. In fact it's one I'll never forget."

Tim saw that Mr Patrick was holding Benjy cupped in his hands. He reached out and took him, felt the softness of the fur against his face, he looked into the little bright eyes. For a moment nothing mattered except that Benjy was back. Then he remembered Miss Jones.

"What I wanted to do," Tim said, holding Benjy safe against his chest, "was just to say thank you, Miss Jones."

Then Mr Patrick did a strange thing — stepped forward and shook Tim by the hand. "It's us who have to thank you, Tim," he said.

"Me?" said Tim. "What have I done?"

Mr Patrick merely smiled his lopsided smile.

Suddenly Tim couldn't be bothered about teachers any more. The glorious summer holidays had begun, and all he wanted was to be off on his bicycle with Benjy. He stowed him carefully in his trouser pocket and rode away.

At the school gates he turned and looked back. They were still standing there, side by side, under the bicycle shed, and for the first time Tim thought — they don't look like teachers at all. Simply like ordinary people, young and happy.

Tim was happy too. Six wonderful weeks were before him, six weeks of sunshine and freedom and happiness — and Benjy.

But why had Mr Patrick thanked him for thanking Miss Jones? Teachers were a funny lot.

*** THE END ***

ODD COUPLE!

On my daughter's wedding day, I had been so busy preparing sandwiches and tea for relatives, that the car arrived all too soon.

I grabbed my shoes from the rack and hastily got ready.

However, right in the middle of the ceremony, the tiniest bridesmaid said out loud. "Auntie, you have odd shoes on!"

I looked down in embarrassment and sure enough — I had grabbed an odd pair in my rush! Nevertheless, they were magic shoes as I danced all night — and even have the film to prove it!

Oh, For A Holiday In The Great Indoors!

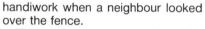

Getting back to Nature is all very well, but a bit of comfort and luxury never did anyone any harm!

MY husband has a bee in his bonnet about getting back to Nature.

So every summer sees the car loaded to the limit, me nursing the frying pan, our two children balancing the cooker on the back seat, and the man I married studying maps.

"Where shall it be this time, dear?" he says blithely.

This is the signal that one of our camping disasters is about to begin.

It wouldn't be so bad if we could settle on a good site. But we started off on the wrong foot the year we bought a bivouac for our son's birthday.

One afternoon we put it up in the garden in the shade of a tree. We'd just pegged in the last guy-rope and were standing back to admire our handiwork when a neighbour looked over the fence.

"Never put a tent under a tree," he advised. "A gale might dislodge one of the branches and you'd be in trouble."

There was not a breath of wind to support his argument but we did a transfer just in case.

Then we found that what was all right for one didn't suit another. I thought the new site was too near the fish pond, my husband said the next was too near the plants.

Our daughter wanted it near the shed and our son sulked because the pegs wouldn't go in near the sandpit. By dark the lawn was like a pin-cushion.

When we got a tent for the family, it was murder. We decided to spend a night at the sea for a try-out. "Back to Nature," my husband said with a clever grin whenever I questioned the wisdom of such a venture.

By JEAN GREEN

We got to the coast and passed site after site. Some were full, others unsuitable.

Just when we'd given up hope, I saw a secluded field, next to a church, with only a handful of tents. It was idyllic.

We didn't have a very comfortable night. The children kept hearing strange noises and every five minutes my husband complained about the cold. It didn't help when I reminded him he was back to Nature.

We'd just dozed off at dawn when the ground began to shake. The tent trembled and there was a shuddering clang like the gong of doom.

Holding his head in his hands and swearing violently, my husband leapt out of the tent in his three sweaters and pyjamas.

"It's the church bell," he said wearily. "Come on, we're going home."

On the way back I said I didn't want a repeat of that performance, but he ignored the hint.

"Next time, I'll choose the site," he informed me.

A FEW weeks later we headed for Devon. One of the camping books described a gorgeous site next to the sea. There was even a picture to prove it.

"We can't go wrong," my husband said persuasively.

When we arrived we turned the book this way and that, and came to the conclusion that the photographer must have been a contortionist.

The camp was on a steep hill and there was a busy main road to cross to the sea. We spent a week defying the law of gravity with the table propped up with a brick.

The year after that, someone in my husband's office recommended a site on the east coast. They knew friends of the proprietors who lived there permanently to keep an eye on things.

The place was booked chock-a-block from year to year, we gathered.

We tried it. It was surrounded by potato fields and next to a railway line. We didn't need to look twice to see the place was chock-a-block. A dozen neighbours could shake hands without leaving their tents.

We left for home the second day, deafened and defeated by the trains.

Sticklers for punishment, we tried Cornwall. A relative had actually stayed on a site there with his family. He warned us about the slope but said there was plenty of room and the children would love it.

It was everything he promised. The field did slope but it was flat enough for tents at the top and bottom so we pitched ours at the bottom.

We were the only ones in our part of the world. We supposed none of the others wanted to drag up the hill for water.

When we looked at the top where all the tents were crowded, we decided it was worth a bit of effort to be on our own.

"This is what I mean about getting back to Nature," my husband said contentedly, and I couldn't argue. The sky was blue, and the birds sang.

The children found some friends and were chatting happily. Then our daughter delivered the bombshell.

"Isn't it exciting, Mummy?" she announced brightly. "A car rolled down the hill last night when everybody was asleep."

We looked to where she pointed and there was an enormous gap in the hedge.

"It was a near miss," we were told when we inquired. "There were a lot of tents down there last night but they've come up here. We laughed when we saw where you put yours. Nobody else would risk it."

Muttering gloomily about a premonition, my husband strode off and began pulling out our pegs.

Too disheartened to care, we spent the rest of the holiday in a caravan.

Since then we've been here, there and everywhere in our search for a site.

It won't be long now before we're off again, and even though I know his intentions are good, the rest of the family won't listen.

They insist we've picked up a new kind of psychological bug on our travels — a mania for moving a tent.

The Day The Lift Stuck...

. . . She didn't panic, she didn't cry, she didn't even tremble. She just smiled at the handsome man who was stuck there with her . . .

IT was a lukewarm invitation. He just said carelessly, "Meet me tomorrow morning if you like. I'll take you out for the day," adding in sudden alarm: "You are a good sailor?"

"Oh, yes." Her voice came through the darkness, soft and eager. "My sea legs are fine."

A nice voice, he thought absently.

The lift had plunged into darkness a few minutes earlier and they'd come to an abrupt halt.

He'd tried to reassure her.

"It's only the current. Don't panic, we shouldn't be too long."

She hadn't fainted or had hysterics. Instead she'd said shyly, "I see you at weekends, going out in your boat."

"Really?" He was startled.

"I can't help it actually. My flat overlooks the harbour."

"You must be an early bird." He usually liked to launch the boat at first light.

"It is your boat?"

"Yes." He smiled. "All mine."

"Oh — it's beautiful."

It was. A sleek red ski-boat that carried him far away from the city crowds and skyscrapers, to the serene solitude of the sea.

And that's when he'd asked her: just because they'd been suspended in a black box somewhere between the 12th and 13th floors of a skyscraper building and he was grateful that she hadn't lost her head.

Then the lights snapped on and the lift resumed its smooth ascent.

She said breathlessly, "I'm looking forward to it — tomorrow and the boat." Her eyes flashed with excitement and he felt a faint stirring of interest.

Complete Story by GILLIAN LAING

The doors slid open. She turned to step through and he saw the winging line of colour above her lashes.

He shrugged. She was just like all the others, completely artificial. He was regretting the invitation already.

They walked down the corridor together, their heels silent on the plastic tiles. He stole another glance at her; absurdly curling eyelashes and long black ringlets — just like a dummy model in a boutique, he thought. Blast, that was Saturday ruined.

He stopped outside the office with "Nicholas Frost" in neat gold letters over the door. "Well, goodbye . . . er . . ." What was her name?

"Daisy," she said brightly, "Daisy, short for Margaret."

HER fingers flew over the keys that day. Everyone complained of the cold, but she didn't feel it. The office tea seemed like champagne and even Miss Murphy who presided over the typists' pool was less sour than usual.

Exultantly, she hugged her secret to herself, like a small child anticipating Christmas.

"Nicholas Frost . . ." she said his name over and over again. "Nicholas . . ." Big and tanned, with hair bleached by the sun, as confident in his tailored suit as he seemed on the beach.

For months, ever since he'd been promoted to the head office from some funny little town in the backwoods, she'd been secretly watching him, hoping and dreaming and waiting . . . and now, at last, he'd noticed her, singled her out from all the others.

She was tempted to shout her news aloud. "Hey! Guess who I was stuck in the lift with today? Guess who asked me for a date?" And to hear the girls' startled cries: "Good heavens, not the Frostbite!" But that would spoil it somehow.

And nothing must spoil tomorrow. Nothing could . . . except the rain. But it wouldn't rain. Even the weather was on her side now.

THE next morning the new sun streaked across the water, gilding the early mists and probing through her curtains to spill into her flat, fierce and triumphant.

But tragedy had struck. She'd lost her slacks. The fabulous, stunning slacks that she'd almost starved for a week to buy, and that she knew drew every eye on the beach to her slender, lithe figure.

The flat was a wreck. Half-open drawers shedding their contents, a turmoil of scattered clothes and possessions, were all evidence of her frantic search.

Maybe she'd sent them out with her dry-cleaning . . . Maybe she'd left them . . . Maybe . . .

But it was useless wasting any more time. She couldn't find the slacks, so instead she'd have to face him in an old pair of jeans. They were faded, shapeless, hopelessly out of date. Daisy wouldn't have been seen dead in them.

But they didn't belong to Daisy. They belonged to Meg and the farm, Meg who was only a wan phantom from the past and had no right to suddenly come to life like this, because she was Daisy now.

Modern, glamorous Daisy: young sophisticate; one of the crowd. Daisy with her own flat. Swinging Daisy who danced at the discotheques and held hands in the coffee bars with a different boy every Saturday night.

But she didn't care about them, any of them. Not the way she cared about Nicholas.

Her eyes filled with bitter tears and she headed impatiently for the hair spray and rollers that lay on the dressing-table.

Then she paused.

Ringlets? On a boat? With the wind and salt spray? He'd want to swim. Of course he'd want to dive over the side of the boat beyond the swells. That's how she'd pictured it; both of them splashing and laughing together in the water.

Well, so what, she thought. She didn't have to swim.

Defiantly she sprayed her curls and began arranging the ringlets.

It was all wrong, though. She realised that immediately. Black ringlets and Meg's ancient trousers were about as compatible as a mink coat and Monday's dirty washing. And as she stared into the mirror, it came to her with a sickening certainty, that her translucent eyeshadow and shimmering new lipstick all went with the hair. Plain, homely Meg in fashionable cosmetics would be grotesque, and laughable.

Slowly she pulled out the rollers, and they sprawled forlornly where she'd discarded them among the tubes and jars and long false eyelashes.

She felt stripped naked. She couldn't consider going now. ►p82

THOSE WERE THE DAYS

When I was clearing out the attic, I came across some old newspaper cuttings, one of which was the newspaper report of our wedding.

With a nostalgic sigh, I read: "The bride looked lovely in a full-skirted gown of Maltese lace. Her veil was held in place by two white camellias."

Romantic tears filled my eyes as I went downstairs to show it to my husband. He sighed gustily.

"Feeling romantic, dear?" I whispered.

"I should jolly well think I am," he replied.

"Just look at what's on the back of this paper! Cigarettes, a shilling for twenty!"

OH, my aching head! I do wish that fly on the other side of the room would stop making such an infernal, deafening racket!

Boy, did I have a ball last night! So, all right, I did have a bone or two more than I should have done, to say nothing of a little too much gravy and milk (oh, did I mix my drinks! I'll say!).

It was my party, and I had all the gang in. Everybody brought a friend . . . though I still want to find out who was so stupid as to bring that great lump of a St Bernard. The way she downed bones was just nobody's business. That girl has real problems: she's all weight and no waste, if you get what I mean.

But the highlight of the evening was the sing-song we had. It was marvellous — all fourteen of us barking so beautifully as we rendered "Down By The Old Mill Stream."

Old You-Know-Who was visibly moved by the song. I can vouch for that, for he moved out of his bed, shot down the stairs, and charged up to us just as we finished.

"Don't ever let me hear that again," he said . . . and I saw tears in his eyes.

I would never have thought Old You-Know-Who was the emotional type.

The party got a bit wild after he'd gone. We played Hunt The Slipper and Postman's Knock. The slippers were rather badly chewed, I'm afraid, and as we didn't have a real postman, we simply had to make do with some ancient trousers of Old You-Know-Who and rip them to pieces.

But let's face it — I don't go much on these mornings-after! Oh, my aching head!

And by the time I've cleared up the bits of bones, lifted all the empty milk bottles, rolled the carpet back, and hidden all the chewed slippers, it's going to be a case of "Oh, my aching back!"

Party? Did you say anything about a party? Well, it so happens that there's nothing better for a hangover than the hair of the human and all that . . . and I'm not doing anything tonight.

And by the way — how did I get in here . . . ?

IT'S A DOG'S LIFE

◀p79
"No," she said aloud. "I can't go, not looking as bad as this."
But even as she said it, she knew that she would go. She had to.
Just one morning to remember. And that would be, not the beginning as she'd hoped, but the end.

ANCHORED in the small natural habour, the red boat impatiently nudged the waves, while he stood knee-deep in the water carefully fixing the fishing-rods into position.

Then he pushed the coolbox of sandwiches and beer cans under the prow seat and looked at his watch. Time she was here . . .

She was late. Maybe she wasn't coming, he thought hopefully. Yet strangely there was a slight disappointment in the thought.

He'd give her five more minutes.

He waded back to the beach where the sand was firm and wet and strewn with jellyfish and waited, trying to curb his irritation, his eyes screwed up against the glare. Far out beyond the harbour, the sea was misty and opalescent, and he wanted to be out there, cutting through the water, the salt stinging his face.

Time was up. Forget her. She couldn't really have wanted to come after all.

He began to move back to the water, then he stopped as he saw a girl picking her way gracefully through the jellyfish towards him.

For a moment he thought . . . But it wasn't her. Surely this was a different girl?

She was breathtaking, with the fresh innocent beauty of the very young, like a part of the early mist and clean washed sand.

He watched her. Her body was smooth and creamy, delicately tinted like the inside of a shell, and as she came closer, he saw that her soft hair gleamed with azure lights in the sun.

And then she was smiling up at him, with eyes as clear and green as the sea.

He stared at her in bewilderment. "You look different . . . what . . . ?"

She flushed and bit her lip. "Without my curls you mean? Well, I couldn't — not on the boat. I'm sorry." She turned away and her shoulder drooped despondently.

"Please . . . I'm sorry." His voice was full of urgency. He wanted to make her feel better, but how could he when he couldn't even remember her name?

"I think," he began haltingly . . . Oh lord, what was her name? Margaret! A nickname for Margaret? Suddenly it came to him, and his confidence returned.

"You look very pretty, Meg," he said softly. "That is your name? Meg?"

For a moment she stiffened. And then, just as he thought he'd lost her after all, she relaxed and smiled.

"Yes," she said happily. "I am Meg."

* **THE END** *

Go PASTA!

When we think of pasta, we think of Italy — even though the origin of pasta remains a source of argument! But there's no doubt that the Italians eat more pasta than anyone else, although we in Britain are slowly catching up.

Pasta is one of the world's natural foods. The best pasta is made from top quality durum wheat and contains a high percentage of protein as well as certain essential minerals and vitamins. It is *not* the very fattening food it is often said to be, so it's a tasty inclusion in a calorie-controlled diet!

Wholewheat pasta has a higher fibre content than "white" pasta — and even more than a large baked potato. Yes, pasta is a full-of-goodness food!

FOR PERFECT PASTA

Pasta is quick and easy to cook, although it can be ruined if cooked carelessly. So here's how to do it the correct way!

For every 1 lb. of pasta, allow 4-6 pints of water.

Boil the water in a large saucepan and add 1 tablespoonful each of cooking oil and salt.

Add the pasta to the water, and stir occasionally with a wooden spoon.

Keeping the water at a gentle boil, cook the pasta for the required length of time (details should be on the packet). Noodles take between 2 and 6 minutes; lasagne about 15 minutes; short-cut shapes between 6 and 12 minutes; long pasta 8 to 15 minutes.

The test: take a piece of pasta and bite it. It should be neither too hard nor too soft and squashy — "al dente" as the Italians call it.

When cooled, drain the pasta thoroughly, melt a little butter in the saucepan and return the pasta. Shake it about and season to taste with freshly ground pepper. Buonissima!!

Here is a selection of tasty recipes to tempt even the most discerning palate!

PASTA

TAGLIATELLE WITH TUNA

12 oz./350 g tagliatelle (verdi or plain or mixture of both)
7 oz./198 g can tuna fish in oil
1 medium-sized onion, chopped
4 oz./100 g mushrooms, sliced
¼ pint/5 fl. oz. double cream
Salt and freshly-ground black pepper

Cook the tagliatelle. Meanwhile, open the can of tuna fish and drain oil into a saucepan. Sauté chopped onion in the oil until tender. Add sliced mushrooms and soften. Season to taste.

When tagliatelle is cooked, drain well and return to saucepan. Add tuna fish, onions and mushrooms.

Pour in cream. Over a low heat, mix all ingredients. Adjust seasoning. Serve immediately. ***Serves 4.***

PASTA WITH BACON, TOMATOES AND PEPPER

1 lb./450 g pasta spirals (or any other short-cut pasta shape)
15 oz./425 g can tomatoes
1 clove garlic, crushed
8 rashers streaky bacon, fried
1 red pepper
1 tablespoonful chopped parsley

Cook pasta.

Meantime, deseed red pepper and slice. Place in a pan with tomatoes and garlic. Simmer for 10 minutes. Cut cooked bacon into bite-sized pieces.

Drain pasta and return to pan. Add bacon and tomato sauce. Mix well together, ensure that mixture is hot. Serve immediately, sprinkled with chopped parsley. ***Serves 4.***

PASTA AND PRAWN SALAD

8 oz./225 g pasta shells
4 oz./100 g prawns
½ cucumber
3 tablespoonfuls french dressing
Seasoning
Chopped parsley

Cook pasta shells. Drain and rinse under cold water.

Cut cucumber lengthwise into quarters and dice.

In a bowl, combine the pasta, prawns and diced cucumber. Toss in french dressing and season to taste. Serve sprinkled with parsley. ***Serves 4.***

Vegetarian Pasta

Spaghetti Bolognese

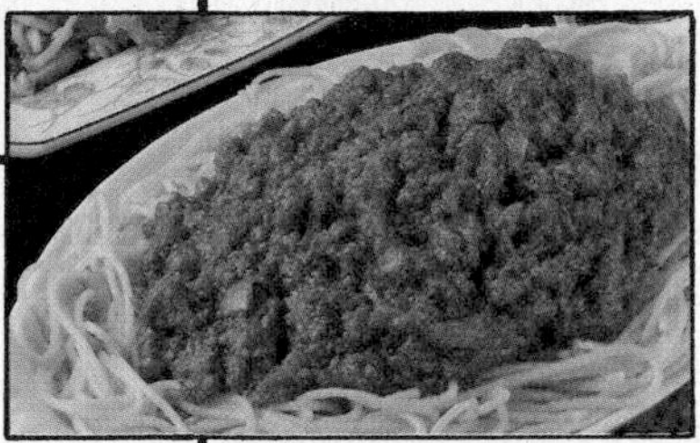

Pasta and Prawn Salad

Brunch Spaghetti

Chinese Pork N' Pasta

VEGETARIAN PASTA

10 oz./275 g macaroni (wholewheat, if liked)
1 lb./450 g courgettes, sliced
1 medium green pepper, sliced
1 medium red pepper, sliced
1 medium yellow pepper, sliced
2 large onions
1 x 15 oz./425 g can tomatoes
Chopped herbs (optional)
Olive oil
Seasoning

Cook pasta and drain. Meanwhile, chop onions and cook for two minutes in oil in a large frying pan. Add sliced peppers and courgettes and fry for a further two minutes, stirring. Finally, add tomatoes and chopped herbs to vegetable mixture and simmer until all the vegetables are cooked. Season well.

Turn macaroni into a serving dish and top with the vegetables. Serve immediately. ***Serves 4.***

PASTA

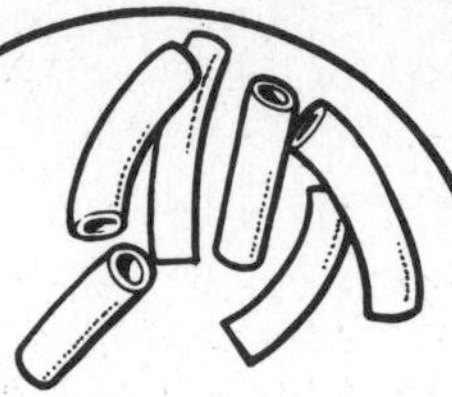

MEXICAN SPAGHETTI SUPPER

1 large onion, finely chopped
4 tablespoonfuls oil
1 lb./450 g minced beef
2 teaspoonfuls chilli powder
Salt and freshly-ground black pepper
1 large green pepper, chopped
¼ pint/150 ml beef stock
15 oz./425 g can spaghetti in tomato sauce
3 tablespoonfuls soured cream (optional)

Fry onion gently in oil for 3 minutes in a large shallow frying pan. Add minced beef and cook until lightly browned. Add chilli powder (adjusting the amount according to taste), seasoning to taste, chopped green pepper and the stock. Cover and cook gently for 20 minutes.

Add canned spaghetti and stir over heat for 1-2 minutes. Swirl a little soured cream over top of pasta and mince mixture, if liked. Serve immediately with hot crusty bread and a salad. ***Serves 4.***

SPAGHETTI WITH CREAM AND ONION

12 oz./350 g spaghetti
2 oz./50 g butter
1 tablespoonful flour
1 small onion, finely chopped
¼ pint/150 ml double cream
1 tablespoonful chopped parsley
Pinch nutmeg
Seasoning
Freshly-ground Parmesan cheese

Cook spaghetti.

Meantime, melt half the butter in a large saucepan, add flour and onion and sauté for 5 minutes.

When onion is soft, add cream, parsley, nutmeg, seasoning and cook for 1 minute, stirring constantly.

Drain the cooked spaghetti and toss in remaining butter. Add to the cream mixture in the saucepan and mix well.

Serve immediately with Parmesan on the side. ***Serves 4.***

SPAGHETTI BOLOGNESE

½ lb./225 g spaghetti
1 oz./25 g butter
2 oz./50 g Parmesan cheese

Sauce:

2 tablespoonfuls oil
1 onion, chopped
1 clove garlic, crushed
1 lb./450 g minced beef
Pinch mixed herbs
Salt and pepper
1 15 oz./425 g can peeled tomatoes
2½ tablespoonfuls tomato purée
¼ pint/150 ml beef stock
¼ pint/150 ml red wine
Chopped parsley

Heat the oil in a pan and sauté the chopped onion and garlic until lightly browned. Add minced beef and cook until browned on all sides. Stir in tomatoes, tomato purée, mixed herbs and seasoning. Add stock and wine and slowly bring to the boil. Simmer on low heat for 45 minutes, stirring occasionally.

Meanwhile, cook spaghetti in boiling, salted water. Drain and add butter. Arrange around outside of heated serving dish. Fill the centre with bolognese sauce and garnish with chopped parsley.

Serve with Parmesan cheese.

Serves 4

PASTA

CHICKEN AND PASTA PAN FRY

14 oz./400 g pasta wagon wheels (or any other small pasta shape)
4 chicken breasts (or large quarters with bone removed)
2 tablespoonfuls flour
2 oz./50 g butter
8 oz./225 g bacon, chopped
1 medium onion, chopped
8 oz./225 g mushrooms, sliced
¼ pint/150 ml cooking sherry
¼ pint/150 ml chicken stock
8 oz./225 g canned tomatoes
1 tablespoonful freshly chopped tarragon or thyme
Seasoning

Cook the pasta. Rinse under cold water and drain.

Cut chicken into bite-sized pieces and roll in seasoned flour. Melt butter in a large frying pan and brown for 10 minutes. Add chopped bacon and onion and fry until cooked through. Add sliced mushrooms and soften.

Combine cooked pasta with other ingredients in the frying pan then pour on sherry, stock and tomatoes.

Add herbs and seasoning to taste and reduce over a rapid heat.

Serve immediately **_Serves 6._**

Mexican Spaghetti Supper

CHINESE PORK 'N' PASTA

10 oz./275 g pasta spirals/twists
1 lb./450 g pork fillet
1 small green pepper, sliced
1 small red pepper, sliced
6 oz./175 g bean sprouts
6 spring onions, sliced
6 tablespoonfuls soy sauce
3 tablespoonfuls sherry
1 tablespoonful cornflour
Seasoning
2 tablespoonfuls oil

Mix soy sauce, sherry and cornflour together in a bowl. Cut pork into bite-size pieces and marinate in liquid for half an hour.

Cook the pasta in plenty of boiling, salted water. Drain and refresh under cold, running water.

In a wok or frying pan, heat oil and fry pork until cooked right through. (Keep the marinade to one side.) Add strips of red and green pepper, bean sprouts and chopped spring onions. Fry for 2 minutes, stirring continuously.

Add cooked pasta to the mixture and the marinade and season to taste. Cook for a further 2 minutes until pasta is heated through and cornflour is cooked. Make sure all ingredients are mixed well and coated in the marinade. Serve immediately. **Serves 4.**

CHEESY PASTA SCALLOPS

No fish in this starter, but the scallop shells make this tasty yet economical dish look very attractive.

6 oz./175 g pasta shells (or any short-cut pasta)
6 rashers streaky bacon
2 hard-boiled eggs
¾ oz./20 g butter
¾ oz./20 g flour
½ pint/300 ml milk
Seasoning
3 oz./75 g grated cheese

Cook the pasta and drain.

Meantime, cut rind off bacon rashers

PASTA

and grill until crispy. Cut into small pieces. Shell hard-boiled eggs and chop. Mix with bacon and pasta, reserving some of the bacon for garnish.

Make cheese sauce by melting butter in a saucepan and adding flour. Cook for 2 minutes then remove from heat and slowly add milk. Return to heat and cook until thickened.

Season well and add 2 oz./50 g of cheese. (A ½ pint cheese sauce mix would be suitable).

Arrange pasta mixture in scallop shells, top with cheese sauce and sprinkle with remaining grated cheese and bacon pieces. Place under the grill for 5 minutes until browned. Serve immediately.

Serves 4.

BRUNCH SPAGHETTI

8 oz./225 g spaghetti
Salt and pepper
4 thick rashers bacon, chopped
1½ oz./40 g butter
4 eggs
6 tablespoonfuls cream (or top of the milk)
Cayenne pepper

Cook spaghetti. Drain thoroughly.

Lightly fry chopped bacon in butter, in the same pan that you've used for pasta. Beat eggs lightly with salt and pepper to taste.

Add to fried bacon and stir over a gentle heat until the egg forms soft, creamy flakes.

Add cream and drained spaghetti and heat through. Sprinkle with cayenne pepper and serve immediately.

Serves 4.

FISH LASAGNE

6 oz./175 g lasagne (verdi or plain)
1½ lb./675 g smoked haddock
1 large onion, chopped
4 hard-boiled eggs
1 pint/600 ml milk
3 oz./75 g margarine
3 oz./75 g flour
Seasoning
3 oz./75 g grated cheese

Cook lasagne. Drain and refresh under cold water. Lay flat on working surface. Cook the smoked haddock by simmering in ¾ pint/450 ml water. Reserve this liquid when cooked. Cook chopped onion in a little oil until just tender but not brown. Chop hard-boiled eggs and combine with onion and flaked and boned fish.

In a saucepan, melt butter, add flour and mix off the heat. Slowly add milk and fish liquid, then return to heat, stirring continuously. Season and simmer for several minutes.

In an ovenproof dish, place layers of lasagne, half the fish mixture, a third of the sauce, then another layer of lasagne, the remaining fish and more of the sauce. Finally, add another layer of lasagne and top with the remaining sauce. Sprinkle with grated cheese. Bake for 30 minutes at 375 deg. F., 190 deg. C., Gas Mark 5, until the top is golden brown.

Serves 6.

(Note: some lasagnes require no pre-cooking.)

Fish Lasagne

Beware OF THE CAT

LIFE gets so tedious, don't it? Ho-hum, it's a *very tiring* business lolling around here most of the day doing nothing. I get so exhausted with yawning and so worn out with snoozing! I shall have to take some sort of tonic to keep up with my sleep.

Mind you, appearances can be most deceptive. Just because I lie around here looking casually bored, don't think I'm wasting time. There are probably lots of things I'm very busy *thinking* about.

Just so as you will appreciate what a strenuous life I lead just in thinking alone, I'll tell you what I'm thinking about right now.

I've been thinking about how much more comfortable this shelf of mine would be if I had a lovely soft cushion on which I could recline. I've been thinking of all the possible places from which I could beg, borrow, or steal such a cushion.

And I have been thinking how much simpler and less exhausting it would be if someone — like yourself, for example — would go and get it for me.

These are but a few of the profound thoughts that rush around inside my brain. I won't even mention to you how often I think about such serious matters as fish, fish and more fish . . . or even of saucers, pails, and vats of milk.

But I have spent a little time thinking about what I shall do for today. And I have come to a decision.

Today I shall be a MONSTER.

As you can see, I am already playing my part. I look ferocious, mean, evil, even loathsome. As a MONSTER, there's no doubt that I am a terrifying blood-curdling success.

Of course, I shall actually have to terrify, to blood-curdle, someone . . . and I know just the right subject. That silly tortoise will try to flash past me at his usual jet-propelled speed . . . and at the right moment, I shall *snarl.*

Oh, I shall have fun being a real horrible MONSTER!

On the other hand, now I come to think some more about it, it does seem an awful lot of hard work — snarling and all that.

Perhaps I'm being as little hasty in being a MONSTER today, when I could be a Larder Robber instead — and with much more reward to show for my efforts.

Liver and kidneys delivered only this morning. I smelled 'em! And they are in that larder somewhere . . .

Heigh-ho . . . 17 paces to the larder, 17 paces back, lots and lots of munching (in a hurry, too!) — oh dear, life simply is very tedious!

X WORD TIME

CLUES ACROSS

2. Have a shot at scoring four Rugby Union points (3).
4. Play for time in the stable? (5).
5. Changes rung in Christmas bells (5).
6. An occupant of 4 (3).
8. Does this illuminant droop if reversed? (3).
10. The twelve of Christmas! (4).
13. Taking, in part, to be related (4).
15. Three-quarters of this time belongs to us! (4).
16. Related — but not to 13 across (4).
17. Christmas show (5).
19. ". . . has caught the Sultan's turret in a . . . of light." (Omar Khayyám) (5).
21. Lively and merry (3).
22. Lamps around to the East for a specimen (6).
24. Where the Baby was laid to sleep (6).
27. A flat strip — of musicians? (4).
28. Past, present, future or strained (5).
30. Cereal favoured by Orientals (4).
31. A type of soup starts this kind of love (9).
34. How we show our appreciation (7).
35. This hairstyle is heavy for certain (7).

CLUES DOWN

1. The tree this puzzle is based on! (3).
2. Lace-makers in rags? (7).
3. Burnt ceremonially at this time of year (4, 3).
7. Where the shepherds saw the angels (3).
9. The animals went into it two by two (3).
11. Bedeck and embellish (5).
12. Reformed character at the end of the "Christmas Carol" (7).
13. Means the opposite (7).
14. This house wouldn't be much use in a thaw! (5).
18. Pointed where I made a change (5).
20. White for tea and brown for coffee! (5).
22. It covers a lot of the earth's surface (3).
23. Illuminated in a polite sort of way (3).
25. One for a top flier (3).
26. A bird that could carry off an elephant! (3).
29. Children love this Saint just now! (8).
32. Suitable treatment for the turkey (5).
33. A Scots boy would start to use it to serve the soup (5).

Solution on p153

1
2
3
4
5
6
7
8
9
10
11
12
13
14
15
16
17
18
19
20
21
22
23
24
25
26
27
28
29
30
31
32
33
34
35

A MATTER OF PRIDE

Of course she wanted to live with her only son and his young wife. But had they asked her out of duty — or love?

THE trouble with Katie was, she could only see Mother as an old woman. Not as a nuisance, not even as a liability, just as someone she was going to accept to please me. And the obstinacy on Mother's part was because she had known Katie only for a few months.

I, of course, didn't see Mother as a grey and thin old lady, irritable with constant anxiety. I saw her as she was when I was a boy — a tall, comely woman, with lots of soft brown hair. A busy, motherly person, always surrounded by kids.

And Katie. Even if we live to be Mother's age, I shall always remember my Katie as the skinny little thing she was that day I first saw her.

Thin, bare arms, spindly, tanned legs, she'd been wandering along the embankment hugging a huge sketching block. She had the most direct gaze I'd ever seen — a gaze that took in everything and sentimentalised nothing. But a few months of marriage had given Katie a few curves and a more mature manner.

"Darling," I said, as we turned the bend and came in sight of the row of plane trees that stood at the edge of the village, "this must be between you and Mother. I don't want to interfere at all, but you will be tactful with her, won't you?"

Katie put her sketching pad into the glove compartment and shrugged. "We've turned our largest room into a bed-sitter for her. She can bring her cat and anything she wants with her. What else can we do, Pete? It's up to her whether she wants to come or not."

I hesitated. How to get over to Katie that it wasn't so much what we

Complete Story by VERA PROCTOR

►p94

◀p92
did, but the way we did it? Katie had been an orphan. Until we fell in love, personal relationships hadn't meant a great deal to her.

"I mean," Katie went on, "there's no doubt about it, the cottage is definitely coming down. All your mother has to decide is whether she wants to go into an old person's flat in Brampton House, or come to live with us."

I smiled — sadly, I must admit. Katie, who was so wonderful with colours, who could see as many shades of green in a meadow as nature had put there, was apt to see human problems in a child-like way — right or wrong, black or white.

"And what about you, Katie? Do you really want her to come, or not?"

"Of course I want her — if you do, Pete! Once, when I was on my own, all that mattered in the world was my painting. Now, it's you. I don't care what happens," she said in that ingenuous way, "so long as you still love me, Pete, darling."

"Ask her like that," I said quietly. "Talk to Mother the way you do to me. Make her feel . . ."

I stopped before the directness of my wife's gaze.

"Make her feel that she's really wanted. Ask her so that she thinks she'll be doing us a favour by coming."

"Of course I'll ask her," Katie said, smiling at me. "That's what we've come down for, isn't it?"

On impulse I stopped the car in the space by the church gate. "Let's walk through the village to the cottage," I said.

"Retracing your childhood?" Katie grinned.

I LOOKED down the narrow road that led through the village. Until the last few years it had been bounded by the church at one end, the little school at the other. Our cottage adjoined the school.

I closed my mind to the building that was now going on, to the feeling that everything was dingier each time I returned, and walked with my wife as I'd walked as a boy, through the afternoon sunshine, down to the school.

I led Katie first into the school playground, then across to the door that led into our garden. I knew Mother would hear the click of the latch.

The currant bushes that bordered Mother's path looked old and dusty, and when we knocked on the open door and ducked straight into the living-room, my throat tightened.

The little ornaments and photos Mother loved looked tarnished, too, and the whole room was dim.

Mother moved in her seat beside the plants in the window, and I saw her gaze go swiftly, warily, to Katie's face.

Katie went to her, smiling, hands outstretched: "Hello, Mother," she said. "We're on time, aren't we?"

Mother smiled — a polite smile that was not soft because there was no softness left in Mother's face now. Her mouth, her face, were drawn. When I kissed her, I felt her shoulder blades beneath by hands.

"Mother," I said, "your room is ready! Katie's brought some curtain samples down. Haven't you, Katie?

"And tell Mother about all the shops we tried before we could find an old-fashioned feather mattress."

"You shouldn't have bothered," Mother said shortly.

Katie said, walking round, "Have you decided which bits and pieces you want to bring? We've plenty of room," she went on, smiling.

She meant to be kind. Possessions didn't mean anything to Katie, but she knew they must to Mother.

Katie looked at bric-a-brac with an artist's eye. She didn't know that the cheap little ornaments had been gifts from children running in from the school next door.

Mother, who'd had me very late in life, loved children. She'd held many close before me, and I shall never forget the way she wept the day the old school was closed for good.

Yes, Katie meant to be kind. I knew it wasn't in her to be partronising. But I also knew that that was exactly what she must sound to Mother.

"I doubt whether my 'bits and pieces' would go very well in your house. I doubt whether I would."

Katie swung round. Her eyes, candid but puzzled, met mine.

"Well now, girls," I said briskly, "which of you is going to make a cup of tea?"

"I," Mother said, "am still mistress — here."

That was stupid, and so unlike Mother. I was about to say something, but when she rose I saw she needed a stick to help her and kept quiet.

THE kitchen with its tiny window seemed dim and had a smell of dampness. Only the murmur of the kettle and the cat's deep purr made it seem the way I remembered it.

Mother talked of things that were going on in the village. But to me it no longer sounded like cosy gossip. It made Mother and her few contemporaries seem like caterpillars clinging to the wheels of the bulldozer waiting to crush them.

"You must admit," I said gently, "all the old things are going. I felt the village didn't look the same as we came through today."

And then Katie cut in with the news I'd been withholding from Mother.

"Apparently council flats are going to be built here, where the school and the cottage are," she remarked. "And you know how soulless council buildings can be?"

"Not while I'm alive! They can knock the place down around me. I won't budge!"

"Well, it won't be quite like that, will it?' Katie went on practically. "You'll simply move in with us. That is," Katie added hastily, her smile coming too late, "if you want to. But you will, won't you?" She floundered. "We want you to."

I'd impressed on Katie that she must be the one who did the asking. But she'd bungled it — asked in the wrong way, at the wrong moment.

"Sounds as if you want me, I must say!"

"We do, Mother. I wouldn't say that if I didn't."

And that was perfectly true. Katie wouldn't. Not with any conviction, not even to please me. But there was something lacking in ►p97

I'LL say one thing for this broken-down boyo — he's a game dog! Yes, I could say that again . . . he's a game dog!

It all started this morning when I opened one eye and looked out of my basket — only to see a blink of sunshine in the garden beyond the open back door. It was horrible, and I hastily settled back to sleep, trying to pretend that the rush of fresh air from the open door just didn't exist.

But the bright boyo doesn't believe in the old saying, "Let sleeping dogs lie." Not him! Besides, why should he? He's not sure — at least, I certainly am not — whether he's a d
or what!

"Oh look!" he yelps in that d
gustingly cheerful way of his. "S
the sunshine! I'm going out to play
with Fifi."

If only he hadn't mentioned tho
last two words, I would have slept c
But I'm a great believer in calling
spade a spade, and so I must confe
this boyo is a rake.

And where a ritzy French pooc
like Fifi is concerned, he's
common or garden rake: he's a wc
ish sex-mad rake . . .

So of course I follow him into t

DOUBLE TROUBLE

ırden. Oh that dazzling, blinding, ıle sunshine! Oh that knife-edged, ·aring breeze of fresh air! Only the ought of poor little Fifi rubbing ɔses with a monster like him keeps e going . . .

Well, it really was a horrifying exhi-tion! The way he showed off!

He went *soaring* over the daisies; ɜ *flashed* across the full width of the ath; he *challenged* the whole world, the shape of one bewildered snail, a fight to the death and he *exca-ıted* a whole flower bed looking for ɔnes I'd pinched at least a week ɜfore.

Oh — and he yapped. And yapped. nd yapped. He's that kind: he has to ɜlp, yap, or yip.

Anyway, I let him get on with the look-how-great-I-am stuff. After all, Fifi wasn't even there to see it.

And now look at him. Done! Finished! Exhausted! He hasn't even the strength to smell a tasty morsel if you were to place it on his nose!

Really, it's like taking pennies from a blind man.

"Fifi!" I coo. "Oh, FIFI!"

When she comes — and she will! — she'll take one long look at me, and a mere glance at this drop-out. She's smart, is Fifi. She knows which of us is still good for some bone-hunting.

As for him — anyone needing a second-best nightie case for a second-best bedroom?

p95 her voice I knew Mother would look for. A cajoling, a respect, a bowing down from the young to the old.

"This is my home. I shall stay in it whatever happens!"

Mother rose with pathetic bravado and, with her stick, stamped out. We watched her disappear into the old school house.

OH, Lord! What did I do wrong, Pete?"

"You just weren't able to see her as she really is," I said. "You didn't make her feel she would be doing us a good turn by coming. People, children especially, in this village, have always needed Mother. She has to feel she's needed."

I caught Katie's shoulders and smiled at her briefly. "It's all right, darling. I'll go after her and see what I can do."

"No. No, Pete!" Katie jumped up and pushed past me. "Leave this one to me."

She was at the door. "Katie — don't! With the best will in the world, you'll probably make things worse."

Katie halted and turned. A finger of sunlight touched her. Katie, who had always walked a straight, certain path, if not an easy one, was suddenly consumed with doubt. Her eyes, which had always been so undisturbed, were filled with uncertainty.

"Let me go, Pete," she said.

I took the cups to the sink and, from the latticed window, saw Katie running up the path to the little gate. I saw her slip through into the school playground, and I worried.

That afternoon I had seen Mother, always so well balanced and tolerant, act like a petty, waspish old lady. A moment ago I had seen Katie, whose charm for me had always been in her singleness of purpose, filled with some kind of inner doubt.

If I persuaded Mother into my home, would I upset both of them?

Yet I knew, as I walked down the untidy back garden with only marigolds now growing in it, that if Mother went into Brampton House I should hate myself all my life. Worse, I would come to hate Katie, because she hadn't been able to understand.

As I stood, Mother's beautiful grey and white cat, Lucky, came and wound himself round my legs.

I picked him up. "You wouldn't be allowed in Brampton House," I whispered.

I stayed in the garden with the cat in my arms and looked across into the little playground. My earliest memory of Mother was of her standing in the playground surrounded by children: her hair, full and soft, caught in a coil at the nape of her neck; her face sweet, her arms softly rounded, wearing a light blue dress and a very white apron.

If only, I thought, Katie could have seen Mother as she was then.

I DROPPED the cat softly on to the path, and walked through into the playground. The door to the school itself was ajar. I pushed it and was overcome with nostalgia — that smell of chalk and lead pencil, of dust in the sun.

Mother was sitting on a wooden chair in the middle of a room still stacked with desks and an easel; sitting in a shaft of sunlight so that the dust in it danced around her.

She was thin and angular and very grey. Her hands, resting on the knob of her stick, were distorted by rheumatism.

I closed my eyes for a moment — no wonder Katie hadn't been able to see her as she really is!

As I walked across the boards creaked, but she didn't move. I crouched down when I reached the chair and looked into her face. Mother had dozed off. As I began to straighten up, I was conscious of a movement near the window.

Katie was sitting on top of an old cupboard, working with chalk on the old-fashioned blackboard. She put her finger to her lips.

Dusk was nearly on us, when I felt Mother move. She shivered, and I felt myself tremble inside, too. For now the decision must be made.

I half turned, so that I was kneeling at her side. I put my hands over hers to warm them, and looked into her eyes. They were brown again, not colourless and faded as they'd been that afternoon.

"Mother," I said gently, "are you ready? Ready to come home — with us?"

Her eyes filled. "You're a good son — I know that. But it's the lass, Peter. It's your wife who must . . ."

Then Katie moved. She stretched her legs and groaned with the pain of moving. She jumped off the cupboard, reached back for the old blackboard and turned it round. She pushed it in front of Mother, and we all moved a little so that the last of the light fell on it.

I sat back on my heels and looked at the drawing. Then my breath caught in my throat. Whatever happened, whether Mother came or not, I was happy in that moment because my Katie had been able to see.

With an artist's eye she had looked through the exterior of the old woman and seen softness and motherliness, tolerance and warmth.

She had drawn the woman I had known as a boy — a comely woman, young and vital. A woman who loved children, and who wanted to give. It was a good drawing, done in chalk. In my opinion it was the best Katie had ever done.

Underneath she had written simply "The Grandmother."

The tears in Mother's eyes spilled. "Oh, lass," she said, "I don't look like that!"

I met my wife's eyes. Hers were as frank as they were on that day I first saw her. "It's not what you look like," she said earnestly, "but what you are, Mother. I'm not a camera — only recording what shows. I'm an artist. I draw what I see inside."

I smiled to myself. This was Katie on her own ground, I knew, but would Mother understand?

Mother's gaze went back to the board and Katie's eyes locked with mine.

At last Mother's breath went out in a deep sigh. "Ay, lass, if you can see that, we shall get on."

Then she chuckled suddenly and pointed with the knob of her stick to the words Katie had scrawled on the blackboard. "And if this means what it says, you'll be wanting a little help, my girl."

"Oh, yes, Mother. I really will!"

"Help me up, then. I must look out a basket for Lucky. If we're to go, we'll make a start first thing in the morning."

We took an arm each and as we walked back to the cottage, my heart was singing.

LATER, in the little room under the eaves that had once been mine, I held Katie close.

"Darling, what happened?" I asked quietly.

She hesitated, then said, "When we arrived — while we were having tea, I looked at your Mother — as I would if I were going to sketch her."

"Old, sharp, very grey," I murmured.

Katie breathed hard. "Then, when you said I couldn't see her as she really is, it knocked me sideways. I wondered if I was only a draughtsman, drawing what things looked like, not what was underneath."

She paused again, then said very softly: "I knew I had to try very hard. For if there was something in your Mother that I should see and had missed — then I knew you would never love me quite so much."

And in that moment Katie was closer to me than ever before.

"And the rest of it, darling?" I asked, knowing Katie hadn't wanted children the way I wanted them. She had always said that if she had me and her art, she had enough. "Was the rest true?"

"Of course!" The old Katie was back, outraged that I should think her devious.

"Pete," she said softly, "when my hands are like your mother's, when I can no longer draw, I should like to have a son look at me as you did at her."

"That shouldn't be too difficult to manage," I whispered.

THE END

By
BRENDA
GOURGEY

Posed by model

THE LITTLE BOY WE HAD MADE OUR OWN

CAREFULLY, I hung a small woolly toy over the cot. We were ready.

My husband, Peter, and I looked round the nursery which, only days before, had been our spare room, cold and empty except for a few crates of best crockery. Now, the freshly-painted walls gleamed a soft blue, and the cot and baby's wardrobe stood brand new on a carpet laid only that afternoon.

It was going to take a lot of love to give Jonathan the security he needed so badly. But love for him was one thing we had in abundance.

Toys lined the mantelpiece and a small pair of pyjamas and a dressing-gown lay on the chest of drawers ready for their new owner. Everything in the room was new and fresh.

Tomorrow, Peter and I were to begin a new life, and an entirely different way of living. Tomorrow, we would bring home the little boy we were going to adopt.

Behind us were six childless years. Looking back, it had been a temporary kind of existence. The lack of a child of our own had meant we had no real stake in the future. Now, Peter and I had a future waiting to begin only hours away.

The early November day was cold, and rain poured down in sheets as we drove along through grey countryside. In our hearts, though, was an excitement we had not experienced before. We were going to become parents, with all the joys and responsibilities that meant.

I realised later that it was a good thing we felt this way. Our contentment helped protect us against difficulties no-one could have foreseen. For, in the next few weeks, we were to need all the maturity, tolerance and patience we had.

Jonathan, the little boy who was going to be our son, was already 16 months old and we had seen him just once before. He was lively and curious, big for his age and seemed highly intelligent. But we had noticed the wary, defensive attitude he had, despite his few months of age.

Mr Stewart, the secretary of the adoption society, had pin-pointed a possible cause.

"We have to warn our foster-mothers not to get too fond of the children," he told us.

Even before I saw him, I had felt that this having to guard against loving must have had an effect on Jonathan.

Just after two in the afternoon, we were shown into Mr Stewart's office for a second time. A small rocking-horse stood next to a cardboard box containing Jonathan's few possessions — a scruffy, once-pink cat, a rattle, a plastic cup, a pile of toy cars and a few picture books.

We heard footsteps, and suddenly Jonathan was there, one of two small boys Mr Stewart had hoisted up under his arms.

"Hello!" I said to Jonathan as Mr Stewart set him on his feet. I bent down to take his hand, but he pulled it away and looked at me suspiciously.

Then Peter took over. He gripped Jonathan firmly under the arms and lifted him up again.

"We men understand each other." He smiled.

"Take it easy for a while," Mr Stewart advised as we left. "You've all got a lot of adjusting to do!"

It was on the journey home that the wary little boy seemed to disappear, and the inquisitive, active child Jonathan really was took over.

The dials, keys, knobs on the car dashboard obviously fascinated him. Jonathan's fingers were everywhere, pulling, pushing and pressing.

For the first few minutes, I tried to hold him down tightly by the arms, but he was undaunted. He twisted and slithered about so much that Peter had to stop the car. I transferred into the back, carrying 34 pounds of determined toddler.

Then, as toddlers will, Jonathan suddenly exhausted himself and fell fast asleep.

For the first time that day, I was able to have a really good look at my new son. His lower lip jutted out determinedly as he slept, and his fair curls fell over his forehead. But I also saw the yellowish tinge his skin had, the thinness of his chin. Even in sleep, he looked cautious and uncertain.

An hour or so later, Peter closed the door of our flat, and we three, the new family who had come together that day, were alone at home at last.

I carried Jonathan from room to room, introducing him, as it were, to his new home. He seemed perfectly happy, and even intrigued.

But it was when I tried to sit him in his new high-chair that he suddenly burst into screams, and struggled so violently that he nearly slid out of my hands.

The same thing happened again when I tried to feed him, and he became quite hysterical when I started getting him ready for bed. As I put him in his cot and drew the side up, his cries rose to an ear-splitting crescendo.

That first night, Peter and I had a glimpse of the task we had set ourselves. And we realised, too, the task before Jonathan.

Peter and I were adults, and able to understand what was going on, but Jonathan was too young to understand anything, except that the world about him had abruptly changed. Naturally he was terrified.

Eventually Jonathan fell asleep, exhausted by the excitement and emotion of the day, but my thoughts kept me awake long after midnight. I realised I had a choice of how to act.

I could either resist or give in to the pity I felt for this little mite who had known such uncertain beginnings. But if I gave in I knew I would spoil him, and I knew, too, how unhappy a spoiled child can be.

I'd always been determined that this should never happen to any child of mine. That, though, had been the theory. Now I was faced with the fact.

BY breakfast next day, the full size of the problem became clear.

Mr Stewart had given me a list of food Jonathan was used to eating, but when I tried to follow the menu, he flatly refused to co-operate. He would either clamp his mouth tight shut, or knock the spoon flying. If I managed to get a spoonful into his mouth, he would immediately spit the food out.

"Baby Jonathan likes to hold a small toy during meals," his foster-mother had written. "It keeps his hands out of the way." Also, "Baby Jonathan does not like coming out of the bath, but a small toy will tempt him . . ."

All this may have applied in surroundings which Jonathan knew, but nothing, it seemed, would tempt or pacify him now.

Any toys I gave him before meals were swept away with one sweeping motion. Some he even threw at my head. As for bath-time, no toy would tempt Jonathan in, let alone tempt him to come out.

Jonathan protested, cried and struggled his way through the first three weeks of his new life. Both Peter and I realised that his every action was the natural one of a frightened, bewildered little creature. Yet, I knew I had to persist. However cruel it might seem, I had to make him used to his new routine.

"He's just got to understand that I mean what I say," I told Peter.

"You sound just like the books you've been reading. 'Babies and children like to be kept in check and respect strength of purpose,' " Peter quoted to me.

"Maybe," I replied, "but can you think of anything else?"

"Of course not." Peter dropped his bantering tone. "It'll come all right in the end, you'll see!"

Peter was right. In the end persistence paid.

At the start of a meal a few days later, Jonathan was threshing about as wildly as ever in his high-chair, so wildly that his head met the wall behind him with a resounding crack, and he was momentarily stunned.

I raised a spoonful of food towards him and he began to shout and shake his head. Then, quite suddenly, he stopped and sat there, glowering at me.

"Have you quite finished?" I asked crossly.

To my surprise, Jonathan smiled broadly, opened his mouth and ate the entire meal without further fuss.

So, I had managed to get Jonathan to obey me. Now I had to get him to love me.

ONLY a few days after we had brought Jonathan home, I found I had actually to remind myself that he was adopted. The joy I felt at having Jonathan, despite the meal-time battles and bath-time struggles, filled our lives and home completely.

Even everyday things now seemed to have a certain sweetness.

One Sunday, I took Jonathan for his morning walk by the river. It was very early and very quiet. A little sunshine seeped through grey clouds and the river was a matching grey, the bushes and trees on the banks almost bare of leaves.

I picked up a fallen leaf and gave it to Jonathan. His little index finger traced along the veins, feeling the texture of it.

"Leaf," I said, pointing to it.

"Ffff," said Jonathan, slowly.

I repeated the word. Jonathan pursed his lips. "Eef," he said, and smiled.

The sudden movement of a white bird caught his eye and he turned to watch it fly until it was almost out of sight. And because Jonathan was looking, I looked, too.

Instead of the greyness of the November day, or the first winter chill, I found myself noticing things like the leaf and the bird through Jonathan's eyes, seeing everything as if it were new and fascinating.

That day by the river was the first time Jonathan had responded to his new surroundings with any real interest. The strangeness was beginning to wear off and his natural inquisitiveness was returning. But in many ways, he still held back, even towards Peter and me.

Already, we both loved Jonathan deeply, and naturally wanted to express our love for him, but the child had not yet learned to respond.

Whenever either of us put our arms round him, he would struggle so much that we had to let go. Sometimes, he would put his head down and butt us away.

"Not to worry," I told Peter, though I was disappointed myself. "He'll soon get the message."

Before long I was proved right, though I came to realise it in an almost back-handed way.

I had taken Jonathan to visit my mother about two months after we had brought him home. One of my cousins was also there with her little daughter of eight months.

"Hold her for a moment," my cousin asked me, and I did so, thinking nothing of it. Just then, Jonathan, who had been playing on the floor, stopped what he was doing and looked up.

"Just look at his face!" Mother exclaimed.

"The Noisy Bunch!"

THEY came, they sawed, they hammered! Oh, how they did hammer!"

That was how one woman of mine described the band of workmen who descended on her house a few weeks ago to carry out building alterations.

She and her husband had decided that, rather than look for a bigger home for their growing family, they would "build on" to their present house.

It had been, she said, great fun and games planning the extension and getting the plans passed.

And then came "the noisy bunch" . . .

"Our children thought of them as bosom buddies. They were spoilt outrageously — being 'employed' as assistants to fetch this and that, and allowed to hammer a few nails in odd bits of wood.

"But the noise the bunch made! I was prepared for the chaos and bedlam of having the house knocked about a bit, but not for the endless whistling and singing of pop tunes, the never-ending shouting of jokes and banter and the dropping of tools, timber and bricks!

"They've been gone a week now. The new extension is all finished — and a lovely job they made of it.

"And you know what? I miss my noisy bunch! Yes, I do! The quiet around the house is positively shattering!"

I was only trying to be helpful when I suggested to her she could always give her three children some odd bits of wood, a few nails, and a hammer!

Jonathan was glowering at me, his brows frowning over eyes suddenly dark with suspicion. He got to his feet and marched over to me, put both hands on the baby's back and tried with all his strength to push her away.

As he pushed, he was mumbling furiously to himself. Eventually, my mother had to lift the baby up in case she got hurt.

Jonathan promptly climbed on to my lap, stuck his thumb in his mouth and, holding my finger firmly in his fist, sat there as if telling the world that I was his.

In any other circumstances, the incident would have been just another amusing small-boy-story to tell, but in Jonathan's case, it was something much more. He had shown for the first time that he thought of me as his mother.

As if the incident had opened some sort of door, Jonathan seemed to become more and more affectionate as time went on. If he fell and hurt himself, he would come running to me instead of just sitting on the floor howling. He went to bed more quietly and he even blew me kisses as he snuggled down with his teddy.

While all this was happening, Peter and I had no rights in law as far as Jonathan was concerned. The first three months were the probationary period required by the Adoption Laws, during which either Jonathan's real mother or Peter and myself were free to change our minds.

"You must be on tenterhooks!" friends would say when they realised that Jonathan was not yet legally adopted. But, in actual fact, neither of us was consciously worried.

The explanation was, I think, that Jonathan had so quickly come a vital part of our lives that we could not consciously believe that he could ever be taken from us.

THE morning of Jonathan's official adoption was windy and extremely cold. We left home before nine and walked along the street, each of us holding one of Jonathan's hands as he trotted along between us.

Over his head, Peter's eyes met mine, and we knew, each of us, what the other was thinking. The picture we made as we walked was the one of ourselves we had always wanted — our little son, walking between us, the three of us together as a family.

The adoption court was crowded with parents and children. Those who were to be adopted, that morning, were anything from two years to a tiny, tiny baby girl of only four and a half months.

All the other children sat quietly beside their parents, either staring solemnly at each other or sucking their thumbs, but Jonathan was no sooner inside the courtroom than he was off, investigating.

He rattled the grilles on the radiators and scrambled up red-carpeted stairs on to the dais. The clerk of the court, a very tall man, grabbed him and swung him down the steps; but Jonathan just went scampering off again, chatting away to everybody.

As Peter and I watched him, we knew that the last of his wariness had gone. He was now just a normal, secure little boy, inquiring and mischievous, friendly and appealing.

He looked different, too. Instead of the pale, sharp little face, his features were now rounded and pink — he even had a little double chin.

Then it was our turn to enter the judge's room behind the main court. The judge, a kindly man in a black and purple gown, flicked through the pile of papers about Jonathan's adoption.

"Well," he said, "that's all right, then."

He gathered the papers together and reached for another file.

I realised with surprise that it was all over. Almost casually, Jonathan had become legally Peter's son and mine. No-one had any claim on him now, he was ours for ever.

All that was four years ago. Jonathan is six now, and a schoolboy. He knows he's adopted, and is even proud of it.

One day recently, he was arguing with Mark, our neighbour's son.

Choice but predictable insults were flying back and forth, when Mark suddenly shouted, "You're adopted! That means your parents aren't really your parents, like mine are!"

Jonathan hardly blinked.

"I know," he replied. "It means that I was chosen, and you weren't!"

THE END

You couldn't have a world of people like Great Aunt Lucy. But you wouldn't have much of a world without a few of her kind.

GREAT AUNT LUCY

YOU'D never believe the things that have happened to my Aunt Lucy. For a start, she is the only member of our family who can boast the rare distinction of once having what she calls her "nether garment" drop down, while she was walking along the promenade at Blackpool.

She was housekeeper for an elderly clergyman at the time, and every afternoon they used to go for a walk along the promenade.

On this particular afternoon he decided to stay at home and prepare his sermon for Harvest Thanksgiving, so Aunt Lucy went alone, and it transpired that he had far more to be thankful for than he knew.

"Blackpool was very crowded that day as it was the height of the holiday season," she said when she told us the story, as she usually did whenever we stayed with her. "And I was strolling along quite happily. Minding my own business," she added hastily, in case there should be any doubt, "when suddenly I felt the elastic snap."

Aunt Lucy was a great storyteller. She used to pause here to let this paralysing fact sink in. Her timing was perfect.

"Whatever did you do then?" we asked, to help the story along.

"Why, I clamped my arms to my sides and made for one of those

Complete Story by ROMA GROVER

shelters they always have along the sea-front, and I could feel them slipping all the time.

"They fell to my ankles as I reached the shelter, and bless me if there wasn't a man asleep on the seat. He opened his eyes the moment I stepped out of them and put them in my handbag.

"Mind you," she added, "he was a gentleman. He raised his hat, wished me good afternoon, and left."

"But weren't you terribly embarrassed?"

"Not at all, " she replied. "I expect he had a wife. It had probably happened to her."

I HAVE always had the deepest respect for Aunt Lucy. She has lived her life the way she wanted it — globe-trotting. She has been a sort of genteel vagrant of no fixed address, and, as I said, you'd never believe the things that have happened to her.

While her contemporaries were getting married and founding families, Aunt Lucy was driving an ambulance in France in the First World War, or playing the piano on a ship that specialised in winter cruises.

She has been a governess in Katmandu and a nannie in Nantucket. She has travelled across the Kalahari Desert and met the little bushmen who live there, and her stories enriched our childhood.

"Well, suddenly there he was, dear, this bushman. Right in front of me. Naked." Pause here.

"A pleasant enough little chap, about the size of fourpence. I said 'Good morning, it's a nice day, isn't it?' because it was, if I remember correctly, and he replied in this strange clicking language they use. They do it by using chest muscles that we Westerners have never developed."

She tapped her chest, which was rather flat under a grey, shantung blouse.

"Of course, I didn't understand a word he said but that doesn't matter. The important thing is, we communicated."

"I thought they ate people, Aunt Lucy."

"Oh no, dear, I'm sure you're wrong. You're thinking of another tribe. Somebody would have told me. Unless . . ." She stopped and began to laugh. "Unless that was what he said. Well, anyway, he didn't, did he?"

No, he didn't. Nobody had eaten Aunt Lucy. She returned to

England and became companion to a wealthy woman who lived by the sea in Dorset, and that brought about another story.

"A very funny woman, dear. She never got up until midday and, just between ourselves, she was bald as a badger! She used to hang her wig on the bed-post."

We learnt a good deal about Aunt Lucy's life from her stories. What she didn't tell us, and what we wanted to know most, was whether she had ever been in love.

She had outlived any member of the family who could remember her when she was young and pretty, as I'm sure she was, because she is handsome still and has a nice pair of legs, and she must be 80 if she's a day.

The general feeling seemed to be that at some time during her travels she must have acquired a lover along with her souvenirs.

She was too loving not to have been loved and yet she had never mentioned it, not even to me, and I knew her better than the others.

This came about because it was customary for our family to convalesce up at Aunt Lucy's. Any illness on a par with appendicitis warranted two weeks in the carbolic air that surrounded her cottage.

Flu merited a week and a lesser infliction was worth a long weekend, and I was the one who had the most lesser afflictions.

Well, this time I had a cold which turned to flu and left a cough, and it was once again my turn to visit Aunt Lucy.

There was none of this Oh, I-live-alone-so-I-don't-bother nonsense about her. She polished her furniture and baked her cakes and read her library books, and when anyone went to see her she opened her arms.

"Try to find out if she's ever been in love or had an affair," the family said, as I packed a suitcase.

"How?" I said.

"Ask her," they said.

"You can't ask an old lady of eighty if she's ever had a lover," I replied, packing a warm dressing-gown. When night came to Selina Cottage, it stayed long and was often chilly.

"Yes, you can," they said. "Be tactful, of course, but there must be a way."

"Well, I'll see," I said. "I'll see how things go."

I WENT to the station and caught the train. The countryside was rich and green, and the trees glistened in the splendour of summer.

As the train rattled along I amused myself thinking about Aunt Lucy's ghost. I had heard the legend often.

A girl called Selina lived in the cottage in the 18th century, she had been witty and beautiful and she rode a big black horse. There was a stable behind the cottage still filled with the smell of old hay and bits of leather harness, stiff with sweat and age.

When the boy she was going to marry had been killed abroad, Selina drowned herself in the lake which lay about half a mile away, just over the hill behind the cottage.

Desolation made her walk into the water and pull it over her head like a shawl, and tiny waves wrote her name on the shore.

No-one knows what happened to the horse. It was all so long ago, but according to Aunt Lucy he still returned to seek his rider. Sometimes at night you could hear the pounding of hooves and then a soft remembering whinny close to the window.

There would be a vague unease in the atmosphere, the faint swish of a riding habit, but when you went outside there would be no horse, no rider — only quietness and moonlight and the dew unbroken on the grass.

Aunt Lucy didn't seem to mind, she was happy to share the cottage with a ghost.

She was waiting for me at the station. It is not difficult to describe her. She looked like anybody's unmarried great-aunt. Tall, upright, hair in a bun, wearing something grey, and nursemaid's shoes.

In winter there was always a ridge just below her hem-line where she had tucked her long johns down her stockings. She saw me and smiled and I went over to her and kissed her. Her cheek was nice to kiss, scarcely wrinkled and smelling of honey.

"Hello, Aunt Lucy," I said. "It's lovely to see you."

"My dear child," she said. She always says that. I don't think she has ever called me by my name, which is Jane. Then she said, "It's lovely to see you, too. Your skirts are getting shorter. I'm not surprised you've got a cough."

"Have you heard your ghost lately?" I asked as we drove along the lanes in her funny straight-sided car that reminded me of a packing crate. Her hands were old and competent on the steering wheel, and her mouth turned up at the corners.

"Well, I had a slight disturbance not long ago. Somehow the vicar heard about it and kindly came to see me."

Vicars were very fond of Aunt Lucy. They thought she was in need of care and protection.

"He told me not to worry, we would fight the devil together and I told him I'm tough enough to fight the devil on my own, given a fair start. I don't mind a ghost or two, I told him. How's your dear mother?"

"She's very well, thank you," I replied.

SELINA COTTAGE was quite big. There was a lop-sided "S" scratched on the outside wall by the front door, a single-lettered chronicle of the girl who once lived there. Inside it was full of sudden bends and sloping floors.

The light in the living-room was made green by rows of geranium plants in full bloom on the window-sill. A long-haired Yorkshire terrier lay on a chair and, curled up, it seemed to have no beginning and no end, like the universe.

"Hello, Caesar, how are you?" I said. I stroked him, and a little tongue emerged from the fur and licked my hand, and somewhere a little tail wagged, so I think you could say his heart was in the right place.

The living-room was not olde worlde and chintzy as you would expect it to be, but distinctly Edwardian.

There were many photographs of young men in the khaki uniform of the First World War, and of women with no legs or waists, only straight long frocks with a big hat at the top and two feet sticking out at the bottom.

All had played a part in Aunt Lucy's life and now only their photographs belonged to her. A green chenille cloth covered the table, and on the mantelpiece two china cats gazed steadfastly at each other across a clock that was marbled and colonnaded like a miniature and very elaborate town hall.

WE had tea by the fire, and after we had done the washing up I went upstairs and had a bath.

When I had finished I put on my warm dressing-gown and went downstairs. The fire burned warm and bright. It was just after nine o'clock. We sat opposite each other, Aunt Lucy and I.

"Now tell me," she said, leaning forward and looking interested. "Are you taking the Pill? Everyone else seems to be."

There are times when she can be quite embarrassing.

"No," I said. "I'm not married. You're thinking of my sister Veronica. She got married last year and I don't know whether she's taking it or not."

"Of course, how silly of me! How is dear Veronica?"

"She's very well, thank you," I said, and I thought all right, if that's the way you want it, if we are going to ask each other personal questions, two can play.

"Aunt Lucy," I said. "Have you ever . . ." I stopped. She looked so innocent. I felt sure she never had. "Who is that young man in the photograph, the one just behind you?"

She turned to look at the laughing young face on the sideboard next to the bowl of oranges. He could easily have been Aunt Lucy's, once.

"Oh, I remember him well." Her voice was low and fond. "I knew him in France. Handsome boy, probably the best-looking boy in the regiment."

"What happened to him?"

"He went over the top, dear, like so many others and never came back. I only knew him for a week."

"Oh," I said. "And who is the one next to him?" This one looked too stern and tightlipped to have belonged to Aunt Lucy but you can't always tell by looks.

"Ah, yes, that one. I knew him for some time. He was the husband of the woman I took tiger shooting in India. He was very peculiar."

"What do you mean, peculiar? How? What did he do?" The thought occurred to me that if he was Aunt Lucy's great love then his being peculiar as well as married would provide ample justification for keeping him secret.

"Well, dear," she said mildly, "for some reason or other, he always slept with a lot of cats and he wore his hat in bed." She bent to poke the fire with the poker. Feather blue flames waved between the logs.

"How do you know?" I asked suspiciously.

"Well, you see, I had to pass his bedroom to reach mine and one night his door was open and there he was sitting up in bed, wearing his bowler hat and surrounded by about twenty-seven cats."

She paused and poked the fire again. "And he was playing a mandoline," she added darkly.

"Of course, I couldn't stop in a house where that kind of thing went on. You have to draw the line somewhere, don't you? So I took his wife on that tiger shoot and then I left."

She paused. "We didn't actually shoot tigers, you understand. We sat on elephants and every so often the guide showed us a piece of undergrowth that the tiger had just vacated."

We sat in silence for a few minutes. The trail left by the man with the cats and the mandoline had led nowhere. Outside, a horse whinnied. It came once, then again. An intimate, calling sound. Caesar unpacked his head and barked once before jumping on Aunt Lucy's lap for protection.

"It's only the ghost," she said to me. "Take no notice and it will go away."

I didn't argue with her. If she said it was the ghost then it was, even though the surrounding fields were probably full of horses who whinnied at night. Or so I told myself.

We didn't hear it again, and she suggested that we should watch television.

"Switch it on, dear, will you?" I did so and when the picture evolved it showed boys with long hair and girls with short hair dancing to a pop group. Aunt Lucy beat time with her foot.

"Very catchy tune," she remarked. "I've seen natives in Africa

Be Careful What You Wish For . . .

OVER the past seven years or so, a friend of mine, from time to time, has issued a cry from the heart.

She's the young mother of three and it went something like this: "Just wait till the last one goes to school. It'll be wonderful."

She usually gave voice to it while elbow deep in nappies or endlessly picking toys off the living-room floor.

Her older relations and friends (me included) used to shake their heads and tell her she was "wishing away their childhoods," or some such sage remark.

But she was unmoved. She'd have time for all sorts of exciting things, she insisted. Oh, the joy of shopping without hands pulling at her skirts. Ah, the peace of an empty, tidy house!

Well, I met her the other day. She had just come from taking her youngest to the local nursery school for the first time.

But far from looking like a woman who'd just realised a heart-felt dream, she looked strangely wistful.

What was wrong, I asked her? Had he created a scene? Had he been dragged away in tears?

"He didn't even look back," she said in a small voice. "I went prepared for hysterics and he didn't even look back."

And as for tears, there were plenty of these. Not from little Gordon — from Mum!

dancing like that when they want rain. Let's talk instead. Turn it off, dear, you can move quicker than I can."

THAT wasn't true, but I humoured her and turned it off.

"Now where was I? Ah yes, young people don't dance the way they did when I was young. In my day we had dance programmes and our partners used to sign for us."

She made it sound as though girls were issued from the stores in her day. "In my day, young men used to put their arms around their partners and sometimes they used to propose marriage. They don't do it nowadays, I'm told. Such a pity."

"Did anyone propose to you?" I asked. "While you were dancing?"

"Oh yes, dear. Well, no. Not exactly. I was going to be proposed to, but something went wrong. It was at a ball given by Aunt Mildred. You wouldn't remember her but I expect your mother would. Anyway, she had this big house on a hill and the garden was full of statues, and Chinese lanterns when there was a ball.

"At that time I had a young man called George. He was an Honourable and a very nice boy, a bit bow-legged because he started riding horses when he was eighteen months old, but apart from that he was all right.

"I had been told he intended to propose that night and he booked every dance with me. Well, we danced on the terrace for a while and then we went into the garden and sat on a marble bench.

"He put his arm round my waist and he managed to say 'Lucy dear, will you do me the honour,' and then he fell backwards into a rhododendron bush, and the last I saw of him were his legs sticking up in the air, and he had a hole in his shoe."

I asked if all her young men fell over before they proposed and she said no, only George and she remembered thinking that if an Honourable could have a hole in his shoe there was hope for the rest of us, and she would not have accepted his proposal anyway.

"Did you come here to recover from something?" she said, softly stroking the dog on her lap.

"Yes, but I've forgotten what it was."

"Then that's half the battle, isn't it? You see this scar on my arm?" She pulled up the sleeve of her grey cardigan and thrust her arm forward.

"Yes," I said. I could see a small indented scar, slightly puckered, like a badly-made buttonhole.

"I received that in the First World War, after one of the big battles. We'd had a terrible day, trying to collect the wounded and take them to the hospital. Imagine it, dear, all that mud and those poor young men and nobody knew who was firing at what.

"I was sitting in my ambulance and this bullet came along from nowhere, just flew through the window. It must have been nearly spent because it merely lodged in my arm. One-third in and two-thirds out. Nothing to deflect it, you see, dear, except my sleeve. It was a great surprise I don't mind telling you.

"For a time I just sat and looked at the blood and then I rushed along to the hospital. There was a very handsome doctor on duty that day. All the nurses were in love with him. I wasn't exactly sorry to be given the opportunity to go and see him and . . ."

"What was he like, this doctor?"

"Oh you know, dear, what you would call 'dishy.' Tall and dark with that lean, hungry look that we women can't resist."

So Aunt Lucy knew all about the lean, hungry look, did she, and had succumbed to it.

"Well I reached the hospital and presented my arm to him and do you know what he said?"

"No. What?"

"He said 'What do you think you're doing messing about with that bullet in your arm? Take it out and go back and fetch another load of wounded.' So I took it out and put it in my pocket and that's it up there on the mantelpiece. I dust it every day."

I looked at it up there on the mantelpiece and marvelled that it had once been in the gentle arm of Aunt Lucy. If it hadn't been for that bullet, and the scar, I would have said that she was the best liar in the family.

"Did that really happen?"

"Of course it really happened. Everything in the world has really happened."

"What happened to him?"

"Who, dear?" She was staring vaguely into the fire.

"The handsome doctor." Digging for Aunt Lucy's love life was hard work.

"I don't rightly know, dear, but it's a very interesting point now you mention it. I wonder what did become of him."

It was no good. I would just have to ask her. She'd driven me to it.

"Aunt Lucy," I said. "Have you ever been in love?"

She threw up her hands so quickly that the dog awoke and barked, thinking he had missed something exciting.

"All my life," she replied without hesitation. "All the time. Be quiet Caesar."

I knew what she meant, at least I think I know what she meant, and it didn't answer the question.

"Yes, I know, but I mean, have you ever loved a man enough to want to marry him and live a lifetime with him?"

Somehow it sounded terribly corny, but she pursed her lips and considered the question seriously.

"Yes indeed," she said at last. "Yes, one or two, here and there. But I never had time, you know. I couldn't do everything. After all, I had only one pair of hands. Why did you want to know anyway?"

"Oh, no reason," I said casually. "I just wondered."

And that was all I discovered about Aunt Lucy. That was all I had to report to the family when I returned. That she had loved, that she had never been out of love, that she had one pair of hands and apart from that, she wasn't telling.

——— * **THE END** * ———

Reina came into my life when things looked their blackest, says WILFRED JENNER, and she brought with her the very best cure of all — the will to live.

IT was 5.30 on a Monday morning just over five years ago that I had my first heart attack. For the previous week I had suffered and had been unable to sleep at nights, but I put it down to lumbago, which was common in people of my age. I was 47 at the time.

While I was putting on my boiler-suit, a terrible vice-like pain took hold of the upper part of my chest and back.

I shouted for my wife and fell back into an easy chair. Between them, she and my teenage son managed to help me back upstairs and got me to lie down on the bed. My wife rushed off to phone the doctor, leaving me with my son.

I can faintly remember the doctor bending over me with a needle in his hand and warning me not to move even my eyeballs.

From then on everything was pain, stretcher-bearers, the noise of the ambulance siren, and a long, noisy ward, seemingly full of doctors and nurses. This thing didn't seem to be happening to me. I felt completely detached from it all.

After what could have been years, but in fact was only days, the fog lifted and I came back to the everyday world.

The consultant told me that I had survived a coronary thrombosis and had damaged my heart. As a result I would have to stay on my back for 28 days, then I could get out of bed and sit on a chair.

I arrived home approximately five weeks after the heart attack. After six months' convalescence I returned to work feeling more or less back to normal.

Less than eight weeks later the whole thing started again — an exact replica of the first time.

To say I was disappointed would be mild, but I fought back and within six months was once again back to work. This time I lasted a week.

The next time I went back to work for one day, and after the fourth heart attack my employers and I decided to part company, the best of friends. At last I knew I had had enough.

The doctor's advice had consisted of only three words, "Learn to adjust."

I know you can adjust to anything in time but after the active life I'd always led I found it very hard.

A diet to reduce my overweight, accompanied by 42 tablets a day, including pain-killing drugs, gradually had side effects, inducing a state of depression. I didn't know whether it was morning or night, and eventually I ceased to care.

One thing I did know, and that was how kind people were. Doctors, nurses and everyone connected with the hospital, which by now I was visiting for a month or so at a time (usually by ambulance at the dead of night), were kind and efficient.

I was carried into hospital, each time not expecting to see the next day, but those people never gave up. They fought to save me with all the means at their disposal, and they made sure I always walked out of the ward and was taken home again.

After a year or so of this I had lost interest in most things and was beginning to feel extremely sorry for myself. I was very grateful for all the help that had been given to me, but by this time I had reached the state where I couldn't really see much point in it all.

My wife and family, my brother and neighbours and my local church were extremely kind and considerate in all ways, but it was no use. I had lost interest in everything. I sat at home and slowly turned into a cabbage.

I stopped taking all but the most essential drugs to see if that would help but it made no difference, except that the pain got worse, and my condition deteriorated.

I was scraping the bottom when my brother, who was a regular visitor, came in one day and said, "We have a Toy Yorkshire puppy for you."

I had never cared much for animals, mainly because I knew nothing about them, so I just thanked him and forgot about it.

A FEW weeks later a tiny bundle of fur, not much bigger than a mouse, lay on my knee and looked up at me. It was so small that I could quite easily have crushed it in my hand. Two bright little eyes stared unblinkingly into my face.

At first I was inclined to turn over her upbringing to my wife, but Reina had other ideas. She clung to me like a limpet and waddled around after me everywhere I went.

The first night was the only time she cried, because we left her in the living-room on her own, in a rather large cardboard box.

Next day, I did the first constructive thing I had done for months and made her a toy out of old stockings and a red woollen hat. She cuddled into this, went to sleep and we never heard another sound.

During the next few weeks she took an ever-increasing hold over everything and everyone connected with our home. She had a heart of gold and showered her affection like confetti, left, right and centre.

She seemed to know instinctively

A DOG CALLED Reina

when I felt at my worst and jumped on to my chest if I was lying down, or my shoulder if I was sitting up. By the time she was six months old she was a picture of silver, tan and black, and every child within a square mile knew her.

She slowly pulled me out of my depressed state of mind simply by refusing to be ignored. She knew my every mood before I did, and acted accordingly. When I felt a little better she was a bundle of energy and I had to play with her or talk to her or simply brush her shiny coat.

But that was about all I could do for her. I had not been out of doors for about eight months, except for periodic visits to the hosptial, so it had been my wife who had taken Reina for short walks. When they returned I would receive the full story, accompanied by tail wagging, ear wiggling and a sort of musical growl which told me a lot more that mere words.

One sunny day, Reina trotted to the front door, looked over her shoulder at me and then trotted back and began her doggy talk. It took a few minutes for me to catch on, and then I realised that she was asking me to go with her!

After talking it over with my wife, I took my walking stick in one hand and Reina's lead in the other and set off out the front door to see the world outside.

As soon as we got outside Reina took charge and bounded and jumped her way down the garden path and into the street.

She introduced me to all the children she knew, all her doggy friends, and everyone else she came across. I met more people on that walk than I had met in three long years.

From then on we got into the habit, my wife, Reina and myself, of walking to a nearby air-field, a distance of some 600 yards, and wandering across the grass until my built-in alarm system told me it was time to return home.

On days when I wasn't well enough to go out, Reina knew what the trouble was and refused to go out with
me. She was content to stay in the house until I was fit again.

One day, we visited my brother and his wife and children. Here, Reina met her mother and sister once again and a grand reunion took place.

Her sister, who had been born at the same time, was as different from Reina as chalk is from cheese. Reina was quiet and never looked for trouble but her sister would fight anything on four legs.

Reina was chased up and down and all over the place until she got thoroughly fed up, came over to where I was enjoying my cup of tea and, in her language of signs and growls, said "Come on, let's get out of here."

She was so insistent that I had to oblige and we headed for home. It took quite a few visits to my brother's before those two came to terms.

IT is over a year now since I was last in hospital and I have been out of doors more than I have been for a long time, mainly due to Reina's pleading.

She gave me the will to live and lifted me, and with me, my wife, out of depression to the understanding that life is to be lived to the best of one's ability, no matter how bad things are.

People tell me Reina is spoiled. I know she is but that is small thanks for the untold hours of fun and enjoyment she has given us. I would do the same again.

And to anyone in a similar situation, I would say, "When you feel right on the bottom, get a dog like Reina."

The End.

Complete Story by AUDRIE MANLEY-TUCKER

The *Wonderful* World Of Wong Foo

It was all just a sham. Under those Chinese robes was plain old Uncle Erin playing at magic. But to one little boy, his uncle's world of magic was very real indeed . . .

THE rain fell quietly, as though apologising for coming at the end of such a golden summer day. It had a soft sound, like mice in the skirting boards, but Matthew, lying in his bed, on his back, staring at the ceiling, did not hear it. He was thinking about Uncle Erin.

Matthew was seven years old. He had a night-light but he wasn't afraid of the dark. He just liked to see his possessions about him when he awoke, instead of feeling the thick darkness press like a curtain.

His mother and father understood that he wanted to be able to see the bright pictures on his wall, the black silk banner Uncle Erin had given him, with the gold dragon embroidered on it in thick silks, the shelves of books, as well as the more ordinary things like his football and cricket bat.

He sighed, feeling miserable. Abruptly he sat up in bed, drawing up his knees, and circling them with his arms.

He wasn't unhappy because Uncle Erin was dead; death was only a going away and a going to sleep. Uncle Erin had explained that to him.

Seventy years was a lot of time to spend doing things, Uncle Erin had pointed out, and when you were tired you needed a jolly good, long sleep — perhaps a year for every year you had spent in being busy.

That seemed fair to Matthew, and he had accepted it. He could even bear to see Uncle Erin's Chinese robes taken from the big oak chest upstairs on the landing, and put into the Museum of Costume.

As his mother had explained in the careful way Uncle Erin had explained things to him, so many people would be able to look at them and enjoy them. He was going with her, in the car tomorrow, when she took them to the museum.

The top rooms of the house had been Uncle Erin's. He had lived there splendidly, his Chinese treasures all around him.

Sometimes, he'd come down to have a meal with Matthew's parents. He was a great-uncle, really, being the uncle of Gladys, Matthew's mother. And Matthew had been taught not to go to Uncle Erin's rooms unless he was invited. But he'd been invited often.

The rooms were an Aladdin's Cave — the Chinese pagodas, the incense burners, the flower pictures, the brass bowls, and the white statue of Kuan Yin, the little jade-green horses.

Matthew was always happy there. His mother knew, and didn't think he was silly to like the colour and magic and excitement of Uncle Erin's rooms.

His father was most pleased that Matthew liked cricket and football. So everyone was happy; except, at this moment, Matthew himself, small, thin, dark-haired and with eyes that saw everything twice as bright, twice as big, twice as beautiful — and twice as ugly as most people did.

"I shall miss the robes," he whispered softly to the shadows that moved companionably around him from the touch of the night-light flame. "But I can go and look at them in the museum, they said. They told me I'd like everyone to see them; but I *wish* I could have had the gong. I wanted the gong."

TO Uncle Erin, the extent of whose travels had been a cruise in a cargo boat off the Greek Islands, the robes had been precious.

All the books and ornaments he had collected during his unspectacular life as an Admiralty draughtsman had reflected his passionate interest in the old Chinese ways.

He had paid a lot of money for the robes, so Matthew had once heard his father say; and he'd worn them only for his exhibitions of Chinese magic.

Matthew's greatest joy had been to help Uncle Erin to dress for his shows. The ritual had never varied.

First the bright red robe, with its tremendous, flowing sleeves and golden dragons worked in thick bright thread. The robe had had to be properly fixed so that the biggest dragon, a fire-breathing monster with black satin buttons for eyes, came over Uncle Erin's chest.

Then had come the topcoat, purple and gold, with more dragons and flowers, and a deep, gold-striped hem. This robe had buttons like little gold balls with loops that Matthew's excited fingers had fastened carefully, in their diagonal pattern across the top of the robe.

Finally, the black-felt slippers with the thick soles, the black skull cap with the red button, or perhaps the black velvet hat with the heavy red tassel — and then the fan which Uncle Erin waved before he performed each new trick; a huge black satin fan with water-lilies and butterflies painted upon it, almost too big and heavy for Matthew to hold.

Then Uncle Erin had been ready, and off he would go to give his shows; usually to children like Matthew.

SILENT WONG FU, the great illusionist. Magic was an art, he could never tell the secrets of how and why. If clever children had insisted he hid things in his sleeves, Matthew would deny it.

Uncle Erin's favourite trick had been the one in which he shook out a coloured silk cloth, and then proceeded to pull huge bunches of paper flowers from each corner, throwing them like darts, so that they opened as they fell to the floor, and stuck there, quivering on their pointed stems.

While he'd waited for Uncle Erin to perform this trick, an anticipation had built up inside Matthew that had been an exquisite, almost unbearable mingling of pain and pleasure.

He knew perfectly well that the flowers had blossomed from the silk because there were pockets hidden somewhere in the cloth and Uncle Erin's hands had to be quick and clever.

It hadn't mattered to Matthew; it was the end, not the means, that had delighted him.

Just as the big, coloured pictures of the Moon Festivals and Dragon Boat and Lotus Festivals in Uncle Erin's book, along with the stories about old China, fascinated him.

But the gong was the most special thing of all. Uncle Erin had never allowed anyone but himself to strike the gong. It had heralded the beginning of a display of magic.

That was the moment when all the breath had seemed to be squeezed from Matthew's body, and he was lifted to a pitch of tension and agonising excitement when he saw the lifted hand, holding the stick with the soft, rounded knob at one end, whilst the other hand held the circle of brass hanging from its long red cord.

"I'd like to keep the gong!" Matthew whispered to the quiet room. "But I can't ask, because no-one but Uncle Erin can bang it, and he isn't here. If I banged the gong perhaps it would belong to me!"

So, the thought that had troubled him all the evening, came back to torment him; a wicked thought.

The robes were spread out in the big room downstairs, to be folded in

tissue paper and taken away, with the shoes and fan and hats; and, beside them, was the gong.

Supposing he lifted it and sounded it just once, so that he would remember the feel of that weird sound, deep inside him . . .

"I *can't*!" he whispered, knowing the terror and joy of wanting so desperately to do something forbidden. "Something dreadful might happen if I did!"

Like what, asked the commonsense cricket-and-football part of him? *You* know it's just a piece of brass that you hit with a stick to make a strange sort of noise.

No, retorted the Dragon-Boat half of Matthew, shocked at such betrayal — it's much more than that.

It can make you feel and see strange things; and it's going to live in a glass case for ever and ever, and no-one will ever hear it again.

The longing to sound just one note was overpowering. If he did that, something deep inside him would always be satisfied.

It would be like Aladdin calling up the genie of the lamp, only *he* didn't want to wish for a lot of gold or jewels, Matthew reflected; he just knew that the sound of that note could seal all his bright, exciting memories of the world of Uncle Erin in the storehouse of his mind for ever.

He remembered how his father had once explained to him that you should always try to do the thing you were most frightened to do. You would find it wasn't nearly so terrible as you had supposed, Dad had said.

He drew a deep breath and looked at the clock by his bed — half past eleven. His mother and father would have gone to bed by now.

He wasn't even sure, as he swung his legs over the side of the bed, that he would be brave enough to do more than touch the gong, whisper goodbye to it, stroke the thin strip of wood that called up the music, and think, with a little sadness, that the house was very empty without Uncle Erin's magic in it.

He put on slippers and went carefully across the landing.

MATTHEW'S mother, lying awake in the warm darkness, thought she heard a footstep but dismissed it as imagination.

She put out a hand to reassure herself that her husband still slept, breathing quietly, beside her.

She smiled. Michael had told her she had too much imagination, like Matthew. And if it was Matthew crossing the landing, he was probably going to the bathroom for a drink of water.

She remembered what Michael had insisted upon, so often: that their son was not to be treated differently from any other boy of his age.

She knew it was good, sound reasoning, backed up by the people who cared most for his welfare, and underlined with kindness.

☆ ☆ ☆ ☆

Matthew went downstairs, feeling his way carefully. He didn't want to put on the lights and waken his parents.

Outside, the street lamp threw a pattern of light across the front garden and through the stained-glass hall door.

At twelve o'clock the lamp would go out; but that gave him time.

The same pale bars of light fell across the big room where the robes lay, giving him just enough light to see by.

He made his farewell to the robes, spread over the big, chintzy settee. Carefully his fingers outlined the familiar raised embroidery that was the dragon, the tree, the trail of flowers.

He stroked it lovingly, feeling comforted by the thought that his mother had promised to take him to the museum whenever he wanted to look at the robes.

He began to feel the first stirrings of pride; Uncle Erin would be famous, in a way, he thought.

He lifted the fan and held it spread against his small body. Then he laid it down and felt for the button on one hat, the tassel on the other, the soft, dull fabric of the thick-soled slippers.

His exploring fingers found the gong; traced its round shape, its dark-gold surface with the engraving upon it, the thick silk cord lying limp.

The gong was heavy. Carefully Matthew lifted it, held it suspended by the cord. He drew a long, shuddering breath of terror and delight, as the fingers of his other hand closed nervously around the piece of wood with which he was going to strike the gong, if ever he found courage.

Already the dark thoughts jostled for elbow room, nudging him. Supposing something terrible happened because he had struck Uncle Erin's gong? What sort of terrible? Too dreadful to think about . . . Just once, for the last time . . . just to let it go, once, making its deep, sad, mysterious sound inside him before it went away for ever . . .

Matthew had never felt so frightened in his life; his fingers were slippery and he started to shiver. Then he remembered what his father had said about doing the things you were afraid to do . . .

He held the circle of brass at arm's length, his fingers clamped tight upon the cord. He picked up the stick and brought it sharply around to meet the surface of the gong with all the impact his strength could muster.

It was as though he had thrown a large stone into a small pool, making the ripples quiver from the centre where the stone had fallen, to the farthest point where the waters broke against the solid frontiers of dry land.

Matthew didn't hear the sound; he *felt* it all through his body, a low, humming resonance, tremendously exciting and powerful; the deep voice sang inside him, hurting him with its full-throated note.

There was a small, tight pain in the pit of his stomach; his thoughts flew in every direction, as a flock of birds rises into the air from a belfry when the first bell-note is struck; nothing terrible had happened to him! Something wonderful was happening!

He was lifted too high above ordinary thought and reasoning processes to wonder if the ripples of sound spread to the room where his mother and father lay. Gladys, shocked into horror for the moment, sat upright, shaking Michael violently . . .

But, downstairs, the gong-note sang through Matthew; the magic had come, and he was overjoyed. He had rubbed the lamp and the genie had tossed treasure into his lap.

He could see quite clearly, the tall, silver-haired figure in the beautiful, brilliant robes with their gold embroidery; the graceful movement of a fan opening to reveal a shower of delicate petals.

He saw too the flight through the air of a bouquet of scarlet and blue and yellow paper flowers, a hand drawing out a rainbow of thin, brilliant silks from a bamboo tube that had been empty a moment ago; hands juggling with heavy brass rings.

Other parts of Uncle Erin, too, appeared to him; the Dragon-Boat pictures, the Moon Festival stories; he saw the red candles, the lanterns and the silk banners that hung in Uncle Erin's room.

It all came back to him, perfectly recreated, with Uncle Erin, smiling, at the centre of it; all from that one deep trembling note.

Even now, as the vibration inside was growing weaker, dying into silence, he still clung to the fringe of magic, with a feeling it would return whenever he struck the gong.

SUDDENLY the light was switched on and there was his mother. She was wearing her pretty housecoat and her long, dark hair fell over her shoulders.

There was fear in her eyes; and, just behind her, his father, looking angry. He so rarely looked angry that Matthew was afraid.

He had done a dreadful thing, he thought. Carefully he laid the gong down upon the settee, and placed the stick beside it.

His father was going to say something; but his mother touched his arm, and half shook her head, gently.

She came across to Matthew and knelt on one knee, so that her face was on a level with his and he could see her clearly.

She put her cool, soft hand on one side of his neck, exploring, and when she did not find what she expected, asked him:

"Why did you sound the gong, Matthew?"

He hesitated. "I wanted to feel it. Here." He put a hand across his middle. "Just once, that was all."

He couldn't tell her any more than that, he had no way of putting into words the magic and wonder that he felt.

But Gladys saw the last of the dreams as they fled from his eyes; and she understood, nodding encouragingly at him.

Matthew answered her look doubtfully.

"Uncle Erin wouldn't let anyone else touch it," he said. "And you're going to give it to the museum, aren't you? I thought it wouldn't matter if I beat it just *once*."

She looked at him and smiled. "We didn't know you wanted it. We'll hang it up in your room and you can strike it any time you like." She made the movement of striking with her hand, seeing his face light up. "Uncle Erin would like you to have it. I expect he forgot to tell us that."

She hadn't only restored his world — she'd given him the passport to that other world within him; seeing the expression on his face, she wanted to weep inside.

She glanced across at Michael, and he came over to the boy.

"You gave us a fright. We heard it upstairs," he said.

"I'm sorry," Matthew said contritely; relieved because his father looked puzzled, but not angry any more.

Michael took the gong and held it out to his son.

Matthew took it as though he couldn't believe it was to be his. Then his mother touched his arm and he looked up at her.

"Bed," she said firmly. "Tomorrow we will hang the gong on the wall for you. Would you like something to drink?"

"Orange squash!" he demanded happily; he squirmed past them both, and ran upstairs, holding the gong against his chest.

And now, Gladys thought, torn between tears and laughter, I'll have to stop him from thumping that gong every hour of the day and night. I'll have to explain how loud it sounds, even though we live in an old, solid-walled house.

Michael followed Gladys to the kitchen and took the bottle of orange squash from the refrigerator and said drily:

"Better put the kettle on, darling — for *us*!" ►p124

MONEY WELL SPENT

Thirty-four years ago, when I was newly married, I bought a broom which cost 14s 6d.

That was a lot of money in those days as you could buy a broom for 6d. My extravagance resulted in our first quarrel. My husband was furious at the awful waste of money, but thirty-four years later I am still using the same broom!

He now thinks it was 14s 6d well spent.

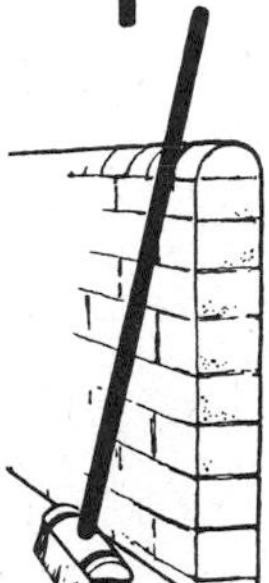

◀p123

BEFORE he did so, Michael came across and took her in his arms, a look of humility on his face.

"We agreed it was best to give away most of the old man's things . . . we didn't want Matthew to become obsessed with them. But the gong! I'd never have thought of that! I haven't your imagination, darling! I don't understand him the way you do!"

"You love him," she pointed out. "You give him balance: with a cricket bat, a football, a bicycle. Those things are as important as the things he saw tonight when he struck the gong. Without what you give him he would be odd, too imaginative, not a boy who is capable of getting dirty, being untidy and is often cheeky! He needs you so much darling, he really does."

"*You* saw what he saw; I didn't," Michael said helplessly.

She left a kiss against his cheek, as she went to the sink, and filled the glass.

"*I* need you, too," she told him. "I have too much imagination, like Matthew."

☆ ☆ ☆ ☆

Upstairs, Matthew sat in bed, his arms around his hunched knees, once again; the gong glowed like a circle of gold in the night-light's pale glow.

And that was the sound he could feel, he thought happily; gold, like the sun in a hot sky, a deep roar like the sea, or the North wind; a warm-feeling sound like a fire in winter.

And now, he would be able to make it all happen whenever he wished. He only had to strike the circle of gold and he would feel the colours, smell the incense, remember the tales, and the magic, secret things that mostly remained shut deep inside him.

Uncle Erin would be glad that *he* had the gong, even though he couldn't do any magic with his hands.

Matthew didn't hear the rain. He took the squash from his mother, drank it all at one go, and pushed the back of his hand across his mouth.

A typically boyish gesture, Gladys thought, amused: part of the balance that Michael gave him.

Gently, she pushed her small son back against the pillow. Obediently he closed his eyes.

She waited for a few seconds, naked tenderness in her face. Then she picked up the glass, and as she moved away, looked with wry acceptance at what lay beside the glass — a thin length of cord, one end plugged into a container that held a battery, the other attached to an ear-piece.

He does very well, she thought proudly; at night, or at any other time when he isn't wearing his hearing-aid, he can lip-read wonderfully well. But the gong — she turned to where it shone in the light from the window — he loves the gong so passionately, not only for the images it can call back into his memory, but because he doesn't *need* to hear its low, vibrant note — he can *feel* it all through his body. It makes him a man who can throw away his crutch and move freely. He feels complete.

THE END

PAUSE FOR LAUGHTER

It does happen, you know. After years of happily being a wife and a mother, a woman can still ask herself . . .

"WHATEVER BECAM

THE postman brought two letters on the day Patricia Carlson realised that she was no longer a person. One of them was addressed to her, a short note from her mother saying that Grandma Ames was failing fast and could Patricia come right away.

The other letter was for five-year-old Janice. It was merely a form letter from a children's book club, but Janice was enchanted.

"Mummy," she marvelled, gazing at her own name on the envelope. "Mummy, someone knows I'm a person."

Patricia put aside her sombre thoughts of Grandma Ames. She smiled at the little girl who had just discovered that she was an individual. What could ever equal this discovery of self?

"I'm a person," repeated Janice, clutching the envelope. "Just like Daddy's a person."

"What about me?" Patricia asked. "Am I not a person?"

"You're Mummy," Janice said. She looked again at her letter, clasped it to her small chest and skipped off to her room to meditate.

Patricia laughed softly. So now she wasn't a person.

Walking back to the sink to resume the dish-washing, she suddenly felt her scalp prickle with something akin to fright.

How long had it been since she had thought of herself as a person, an individual personality?

She was in the habit of thinking of herself as a wife, a mother, a Sunday school teacher, cook, gardener, chauffeuse, seamstress.

She was a chameleon-creature, changing from one rôle to another as necessity demanded.

She was a 41-year-old mother of four children. But what had happened to the person she had once been?

Patricia stared at her hands, submerged in the dish-water. Grandma would know what had happened to her. They had always understood each other, the ageing woman and the blithe young girl.

Patricia had been called Pat then.

PATRICIA sloshed the dishcloth across a plate. Remembered how she had run to Grandma when her parents couldn't understand why she should want to go to an art school in another town.

After all, the college right there in town was just as good. Why did she want to leave home and go off somewhere so many miles away?

"Some folk are home-lovers," Grandma had said. "They decide the moonlight looks just the same on their side of the mountain as it does on the other side. But some of us have to go away from all that's familiar to find out more about ourselves. Sort of hone ourselves on the whetstone of the world, you might say."

OF ME?"

Complete Story by

LAEL J. LITTKE.

Grandma had smiled at Pat, the young, eager Pat, so impatient to be off to discover herself.

"You're so much like me, Pat. I wanted to go away, too, when I was young. I could sing a little, and I wanted to study for a singing career. But then I met Will Ames at a church picnic, and that was that." Grandma patted her granddaughter's hand. "After all, the nicest part of going away is coming home again," she said.

After Grandma had talked to Pat's parents, they agreed to let her go to the art school she wanted.

Then she met John Carlson and married him, settling down in that city miles away from her family. She had been happy, so happy that she didn't even remember when the eager, independent young Pat had disappeared, to be replaced by a middle-aged woman, a little overweight, a little tired and harassed, a little grey.

A woman who scarcely even thought of herself any more. A woman called Patricia.

Patricia's reverie was broken by a tug at her skirt. It was one of the many children who passed through the house all day long.

"Janice's mother," said the little girl in a red ribbon, "where is Janice?"

"I think she's in her room, Janice's friend," said Patricia.

So we're even, she chuckled to herself. Neither of us has an identity.

She watched the solemn little girl walk out of the room.

I'm just Janice's mother to her, she thought. To Joann's friends I'm Joann's mother. I'm also Denise's mother. And Bob's. I'm John's wife. But who am I?

She didn't tell her family about not being a person. The children, from 16-year-old Joann to five-year-old Janice, would just be puzzled.

And John? Was she a person to John? Or was she just someone who was always there? She decided not to mention it to him, either. It was something she needed to settle for herself.

Janice showed her letter to the rest of the family. Everyone laughed indulgently when Janice refused to let anyone else so much as touch it.

Bob recalled how when he was little (exactly two years ago) he ►p128

WHO SAYS...

...IT'S NICE TO GET UP IN THE MORNING

IT'S nice to get up in the morning," the old music-hall song says, "but it's nicer to stay in bed," and most people would tend to agree with the latter opinion.

For, apart from the freakish few who can — and do — leap out of bed at the first chink of light or the first buzz of the alarm clock, getting up in the morning is a wrench that has to be endured.

Yet why should most of us crave that extra 10 minutes in bed? What makes us feel so unenthusiastic about getting up? Perhaps if we know a little about what happens when we sleep, it may help us to answer these questions.

When we drop off to sleep at night our various faculties, each controlled by different sections of the brain, relax in a fixed order.

First to go is will-power, followed slowly by reasoning, memory, imagination and the sense of smell. Hearing, touch and movement are the last to relax, and as we all know, these sleep very lightly.

On waking in the morning, the reverse order is followed, so will-power is the last faculty to rejoin us. No wonder it's difficult for the brain to order us to get up whenever we're conscious we should!

We must also remember that, although our sense of hearing ha returned, our sense of time has no Consequently, those "few minute more" may turn out to be half a hour unless we are careful.

Another factor that affects ou morning habits is the now firml established idea of our sleeping i marked waves or "valleys."

We sleep most soundly during th first hour, usually before midnight Deepness of sleep then wanes an waxes again, perhaps twice, befor about the seventh hour.

◄p127

had received a letter from Grandma Ames. He had been so proud, he said, he kept it in his treasure box.

Patricia brought out the letter from her mother and read it to John and the children. Although none of them had seen Grandma very often, they were all sorry to know that she was ill.

They agreed that Patricia should go to her bedside as soon as possible. Of course they could get along while she was away. She knew they were trying to make it easier for her to leave, but in her present touchy frame of mind she wondered if they would even miss her.

Thinking about it later, Patricia decided the trip would serve several purposes.

She could, as Grandma had said years ago, once more remove herself

avid Gunston offers some easons as to why some of us greet ne morning bright and cheerful vhile others want only to be left to uffer in silence!

By then, many people are deep in nother sleep valley.

This can be proved by regularly hecking the body temperature, 'hich falls during deep sleep and ses when wakefulness is near.

A DEFINITE body rhythm such as this, divides us all into two separate categories: "day" eople and "night" people, or, as a amous physician once termed them - "larks" and "owls."

"Day" people, or "larks," are those 'ho find least difficulty in waking and etting up, because their rising time oincides with the crest of a sleep alley, when they are nearest to onsciousness.

Although no-one is fully awake 'hen he or she gets up, or is ompletely normal in such things as ody temperature, blood pressure nd speed of reflexes, these "larks" uickly reach par and are soon at neir working efficiency peak.

On the other hand, the "night" people, or "owls" are often deep in a sleep valley when they should be getting up.

When they do finally rise, they are below par, perhaps for several hours, grouchy, drowsy and resentful of having to wake at all.

Yet these people — and research seems to indicate they form the majority — reach an efficiency peak by midday as a rule and can carry on late into the night.

Despite all its recent probing of the whys and wherefores of sleep, science cannot explain how it is that some lucky people can fall off to sleep at bedtime, certain that they will wake on the dot at 6.15 or 8.15 or whenever it has to be — just like that.

Perhaps it's connected with the discovery that each tiny cell of our bodies may contain a tiny biological clock — an innate sense of rhythm which marks time every hour of our lives.

So far, however, it isn't clear why only a few people can set these invisible timekeepers at will.

Perhaps, one day, further investigation will enable us all to become happy, on-the-dot wakers. Then, and probably only then, will it really be nice to get up in the morning!

The End.

from her familiar surroundings and perhaps rediscover who she was. Perhaps she could find out what had happened to Pat Ames, who was once a person.

GRANDMA looked tiny and fragile in her enormous bed. She was 92. The little lady who had always been full of vitality, who had scampered about fixing dinner for 10 people, was so quiet now.

"She's not in any pain," her mother whispered into Patricia's ear as they stood looking at Grandma. "It's as if she's worn out all of a sudden."

Patricia fought back the tears and walked towards the bed. Her mother put a hand on her arm.

"She may not know you," she cautioned. "Sometimes she's a little vague. Sometimes she says she doesn't know who she is."

Patricia nodded and walked to the bedside. She picked up the hand which lay, inertly, on the white coverlet.

"Grandma," she said. "It's Patricia."

Grandma opened her eyes slowly, as if she were very tired.

"Patricia?' her voice was like the tinkle of a tiny silvery bell.

She gazed at Patricia through the blue, blue eyes which had been the envy of all her granddaughters.

"Patricia," she sighed, "I don't know who I am any more."

Mrs Ames gave Patricia a "see-what-I-mean" look. "Grandma," she said, "you'd better sleep now."

Grandma shifted restlessly. "Grandma," she whispered. "Who is Grandma?" The frail hand picked at the coverlet. "If Will were here he would know who I am. Will would tell me."

"We'd better go now," Patricia's mother said.

"Let me stay just a few minutes, Mother," Patricia whispered. Her mother tiptoed from the room.

PATRICIA looked at Grandma again. Was it because she was so like her gran that she understood? Could no-one else think of her as someone other than Grandma?

"Of course you know who you are," Patricia said softly. "Melissa Mary Bartlett, the prettiest girl in town."

The blue eyes looked questioningly at her.

"Melissa Mary, with the crow's-wing hair. Melissa Mary, with the summer-sky eyes and the tiniest feet."

Patricia stroked the hair which was soft and white, like pure silk. "Remember, Melissa Mary, when you wore the cornflower-blue dress at the church picnic and saw your Will for the first time?"

Grandma had told her so many times the story of the picnic.

"I knew how I looked in that dress," Grandma said. "Selina Courtney didn't have a chance."

Patricia thought she had gone to sleep. Then the blue eyes opened again.

"Patricia." The soft voice was barely audible, Grandma smiled and closed her eyes, and in repose her face was peaceful. "I wasn't always Grandma," she whispered, before she drifted off to sleep.

"I know," Patricia said. "I know." She stroked the tiny hand and held it until she was sure Grandma was asleep. "Goodbye, Melissa Mary."

Grandma died quietly in her sleep that night. Much as Patricia would miss her, she was glad Grandma had gone on to rejoin her Will with the memory of herself as the blue-eyed girl Will had first seen and loved. She knew Melissa Mary's homecoming had been a happy one.

Patricia thought a lot about herself and Grandma in the next few days. She had come hoping that Grandma could help her one more time, but, instead, she had been able to help Grandma.

When you were young you concentrated on taking whatever would help you as a person. As you grew older you began giving, and in doing so forgot yourself. But did this make you less of a person? Was not the giving of oneself better than the discovery of self? Did it not indicate that you had become a bigger and better person, possessing qualities you had not dreamed you possessed?

Patricia hadn't completely solved her problem by the time she boarded the train for home, but she found it being pushed to the back of her mind by the prospect of seeing her family again.

THEY were waiting for her on the platform. John managed to look dignified despite his eager grin. Bob and Janice waved, and Joann smiled dreamily at the train as it slowed and stopped.

Why, she's like I used to be, Patricia thought. Dreaming of the time she can board a train or plane and be off to see the world.

Denise, who stood there trying to be grown up but wanting to shout with joy like the younger children — Denise's black hair was just like Pat's had once been, and like Melissa Mary's must have been.

Young Pat is gone, Patricia thought, whisked away by time, yet she is preserved in my children.

She was scarcely off the train before the children were swarming over her, laughing, kissing her, welcoming her back.

Janice handed her the tattered remnants of her letter, the symbol of her discovery that she was a person. "I want you to have this," she whispered.

Patricia's heart was full as she listened to the happy chatter of their adventures in her absence. She could never doubt again that she was a person, a Very Important Person, in their eyes. If Pat was gone, then the compensations were well worth the loss.

But was she gone? What was she really? Could she not recapture, as Grandma had, the memory of a former self? Surely that old zest for seeking and learning must exist somewhere, mingled in with the busy wife, mother, Sunday school teacher, who was Patricia.

The years that the children are dependent on you are so very brief, she thought. You brought them into the world and then were caught up in teaching and guiding and caring for them. Before you realised it, they were going to school. Then they were off to seek their own places in the world, leaving you wondering what to do with this person who had been so happy and absorbed in mothering them. So much so, you had forgotten there was any other way of life.

Janice would be starting school in another month. Would not this be a splendid time to rekindle Pat's old interest in art?

Perhaps she and John could take that dreamed-of trip, to see if the moonlight on the rooftops of Paris was as exciting as it sounded.

Life was wonderful, Patricia decided. The past had been busy and happy, and the years ahead were filled with promise, just as they had seemed to Pat so long ago. Nothing then, really, had happened to Pat, except that she had travelled some miles.

John had been standing quietly to one side, waiting for the children to finish their greetings. Now he came forward and handed her a single red rose, just like the first flower he had ever given her.

"Welcome home, Pat," he said, with a smile.

As she looked into his eyes and smiled back, Patricia knew what Grandma meant when she said her Will would know who she was.

* **THE END** *

The SANCTUARY

Did she want the cottage as her home for the future . . . or as a place to hide from the past?

Complete Story by SUSAN SALLIS.

I FELL for the cottage immediately. It was squat, with a steep roof that ought to have been thatched and the ruins of a rusty pump at the back door.

"Of course the water's piped, Mrs Newark," the agent said quickly when he saw my eye on it. "At least downstairs. Probably you could get a grant for bathroom conversion." The way he said it I knew I could forget about a bathroom.

But the tiny walled-off corner of the kitchen which housed the copper would take a shower, probably. Anyway, I was on my own during term time, and my son, Dennis, had a 12-year-old's healthy dislike of baths.

"What's the lowest figure they'll take?" I asked, trying to sound crisp and businesslike and not in the least like a woman whose husband had left her for someone younger and prettier and altogether more desirable.

The agent began to hedge. "It's run down, of course. But if you could spend a bit on it . . ."

I couldn't.

". . . it would make a delightful weekend cottage. Quite a retreat from the madding crowd."

"How much?" I persisted. It was mid-October and very cold in the flag-stoned kitchen. I wondered whether coal lorries could get down the rutted lane which the agent's car had negotiated at five miles an hour. I wondered whether Dennis would approve of being quite so far from . . . anything.

"He might drop under the eighteen thousand for a genuine quick sale," the agent said, as if he were giving me a Christmas present. Even selling everything, I couldn't raise more than 15 thousand.

"Where does he live? I'll go and see him."

Apparently this wasn't acceptable. "Bruce Kershaw particularly wants to be left out of any transactions. However, if you want to make an offer, Mrs Newark, I'll get in touch with him."

"Fifteen thousand," I said, without preamble, unable to bear the haggling that would result if I voiced my opinion that the cottage wasn't worth half that. Did he think for one moment that if I had 18 thousand pounds I would put up with cold taps, stone floors and a grate that might have been hammered out of an oil can?

I wandered outside while he spluttered over my offer and looked again at that huddled protective roof and the orange leaves in drifts under the tiny winking windows. Perhaps I would.

The cottage had the look of a sanctuary and I felt the ache in my heart — which I had diagnosed a long time ago as merely wounded pride — ease a little at the stubborn permanence of it.

The agent joined me and we both stared.

"We'll get in touch with you during the next few days."

HE drove me back to the village, where I had left the car, and offered me tea in his one-man office. I refused and imagined for a moment that he looked rebuffed. I wondered what was happening to me that I could no longer accept anything, not even an invitation from a house agent to a cup of tea in his office.

I thought of the cottage and wanted it desperately. I wanted to love something again wholeheartedly, and I could love that cottage with no strings attached. I remembered Dennis with intense guilt. But even Dennis and his couldn't-care-less affection was suspect.

We never talked of Brian so I didn't know whether he minded not having a proper father any more, or what he made of the fact that after being part of a family he was now left with only me. Good old Mum.

I got out of the car again and went into a telephone kiosk nearby. Matron answered and said she would fetch Dennis, he was watching the wrestling.

"Mum?" He sounded a little lost. "Any luck?"

I could see him, his hair straight and silky, his round face still a small boy's, his hands on the phone strangely a man's. I became over-enthusiastic.

"You'll love it, Dennis. It's proper country, miles of it. And the cottage itself is quaint and old fashioned. Not even a bathroom . . ."

"Super!"

I knew that would appeal to him.

"Could I have a pony, Mum? Fielding has a pony and they go trekking in the holidays."

"Well, I don't know. Where would we keep it?"

"I thought you said we had a lot of land? Couldn't we build a stable somewhere. Or something?"

I said, terribly patient, "There is land, of course. Miles of it, but it isn't ours. I get the impression this was a farm labourer's cottage, but where the farm is I've no idea."

"A farm labourer's cottage?" Dennis sounded disenchanted.

"Yes. There's quite a bit needs doing. Painting, things like that. We'll be pioneers."

His silence was sceptical.

"There's something so attractive about it, Dennis," I went on. "Like the gingerbread house."

A couple of years ago he might have laughed at that. Now he said politely, "It sounds nice." We talked then of new pyjamas and I promised I would meet him next Saturday afternoon.

"Have a good week, darling. Work hard."

"I always do." He managed a proper laugh, but he didn't wish me luck with the cottage.

Strangely that made me want it even more. I was certain that Dennis needed a proper home as much as I did. His school holidays were a continual fête for us both. My landlady didn't approve of children in the flat, so we divided the time assiduously between my parents and my mother-in-law.

My parents were over-full of sympathy and fixed up a round of outings and treats in which Dennis met suitable friends and I met suitable suitors. Brian's mother was full of guilt and compensated by fixing up a round of outings and treats . . .

I WENT back home and waited. I wanted the cottage more and more. My nights now were filled with weird dreams of selling marzipan cottages across the counter to a boy who looked like Dennis and never even tasted them before throwing them away.

The first week in November was half term and I was glad to escape to my parents' solid detached residence in suburbia. Our first evening there Mother whisked Dennis into the kitchen to help with the dishes so that Father and I could have our usual business chat.

"Dennis will be fourteen in just over a year," my father said. "Have you thought about another school? I sent for a prospectus — nothing too expensive."

"It's good of you, Dad. But I'm not sending Dennis to boarding school next year."

His dear face wrinkled into lines of concern. "How will you manage, Sarah? The flat and your job . . . ?" He brightened. "Were you thinking of living with us, my dear?"

"No, it wouldn't do, Dad. I've marked time for two years. I must make another home, start again. I've got my eye on a cottage. It's cheap. I might have to ask you for a small loan."

The following week brought no letter from the house agent and as soon as I had taken Dennis back to school, I rang him. He sounded sincerely apologetic.

"Actually, Mrs Newark, between you and me, I think the owner is hanging on for a better offer. I've written twice and simply had no reply. Of course, Bruce Kershaw is a very busy man."

"But his secretary would deal with his correspondence?" I angled.

"Exactly. Several of his letters have been signed by his secretary, in fact. I'll write again and say that you have another property in mind."

"Which is true."

"Quite." He knew I was lying.

I drove to the agency to collect my next assignment and drank their coffee while I leafed through their telephone directories. *Kershaw, Lane & Adams, Bdg. Cts.* stood out clearly because it was so long. I noted the number without making any definite plans. The next three days were leaden.

I tapped my way through eighty thousand words betweeen looking out of the window and worrying about Dennis. A letter came from Mother-in-law. Brian and his wife were spending Christmas with her and would it be possible for Dennis to come for a day? Poor Mother-in-law, torn in little pieces.

I wrote back and said of course, and when Dennis and I were settled in our country cottage she must come and have a holiday with us. And then I telephoned Kershaw, Lane & Adams and made an appointment to see Mr Kershaw about some building I was considering in Essex.

The offices were in a big chromium-plated block near the river. The foyer reminded me of a store with people everywhere and the six lifts opening and closing like crazy Jack-in-the-boxes.

When I stepped out on the fifth floor there were carpets and ashtrays on stands, and strip lighting over one or two crazy pictures, and I felt claustrophobic and very nervous. A girl behind a desk got up and took me to a door immediately, before I could step back into the lift.

"You telephoned yesterday, Mrs Newark? Mr Kershaw is free. He never keeps clients waiting." She smiled roguishly, as if I were in for a treat which she enjoyed regularly and didn't mind sharing. She was blonde and leggy and in that instant I could imagine exactly what Bruce Kershaw was like.

I wasn't disappointed. He was behind a desk, too. He took in my fur coat — a relic of married days — and came forward like a family friend to take my hand and lead me to the vast window overlooking the river.

"We'll have coffee now, Jackie," he said. If I hadn't labelled him insincere from the inside out, I'd have liked his voice. It was light and easy and full of confidence.

That's how he was, a man of average height, compact and good to look at, darkish, probably a good dancer, a go-anywhere-talk-to-anyone sort of man. I felt all the barriers rise inside me.

NOW, Mrs Newark." I was the next item on his itinerary. He smiled with reserved charm and sat down briskly to indicate he wasn't going to waste my time or money. "About this home you would like in Essex. Have you a plot in mind?"

"Yes." I wished I hadn't come.

"You already have some ground?"

"Not exactly. There is a piece for sale. Half an acre but a very narrow road frontage. Twenty feet at the most."

He made a whistling mouth. "Tricky to plan anything on that scale, Mrs Newark. Any hope of purchasing an extra width?"

I shook my head. "There's a cottage already on the land. Practically derelict."

"Ah. That means water and electricity already there."

"Water. Nothing else."

"Never mind, it will keep the price down. Have you made an offer?"

"Fifteen thousand."

He whistled silently again. "I must say you're keen, Mrs Newark. Well, as you know, this firm is concerned entirely now with municipal building, but I have always had a special place in my heart for homes. Especially bijou homes."

I really did hate him now. He was talking to my fur coat.

"I have one or two stock drawings here." He moved lightly to his desk and opened a drawer. "But with such an unusually narrow boundary I'd like to have time to dream up something really special . . ."

Jackie came in with coffee and put it on the low table. Then she produced some letters for signature and the mid-morning post. Then she said, "I've seen to the birthday card for Miss Dalrymple and the flowers for your aunt."

"I'm sorry," I said quickly. "I should have told you. But I thought you wouldn't listen. The house agent said you wouldn't reply to his letters."

"Newark. I knew I'd seen the name somewhere."

I felt anger must erupt at any minute, so I gabbled. "It's like this. I must have a home — my son's at boarding school and it's not good for him. If I could buy this place, he could go to the local school and I could give up my job — maybe there'd be farm work in the summer or something. And we could concentrate on being a family again."

"Thank you, Jackie." He patted her arm and she smiled into his eyes and left.

"Um. Where were we?"

"At my bijou residence."

He looked at me sharply. "I shall have to see the land, Mrs Newark."

"Of course." That would give me breathing space. At least I wasn't to be thrown out of his office. If he saw the place again he might even realise it wasn't worth 18 thousand. I was surprised at such personal attention. It was the fur coat, of course.

He was still looking at me. "Perhaps you and your husband would care to come with me? Then you could show me exactly what you want."

In spite of myself, I flushed. "I haven't got a husband, Mr Kershaw. We're divorced."

He simply nodded. "I see. Well, how about you, then? It would save a lot of time."

I nodded and fumbled with my coffee spoon. He flicked a switch on his desk and spoke to Jackie. It seemed we were going right away.

He came back to the window and drank his coffee in one draught. Then he sat down and flashed a proper smile at me.

"You've no idea what fun it will be to get away from here and start planning a real home again. My partners would call me small minded. I am. Or is it my terrific ego trying to build my personal monument?"

I couldn't help smiling back.

"It's the primeval nesting instinct," I said. "We need homes like snails need shells."

"Protection? Somewhere to hide?" He was trying to sum up what was inside the fur coat now and he'd come very close to the truth.

His car was flamboyant. Long and open. He passed me a headscarf from the glove compartment and I fingered it doubtfully hoping it wouldn't smell of someone else's perfume.

"It's Jackie's," he said. I flushed again.

THE trip took an hour, and apart from issuing directions we didn't talk much. I seemed to feel his silence grow deeper as we roared through the village and bounced down that awful lane. He must have known by then, but he kept going until we stopped outside the ridiculously prim gate and the strip of tattered garden which hemmed the cottage in.

"I'd forgotten what a hovel it was," Bruce Kershaw said at last.

I liked him for that. I felt that if ever he lost — which was unlikely — he'd be a good loser. ►p138

THE THINGS KIDS SAY

HIGH SPIRITS!

One time when I was ill, I found a hot whisky and lemon juice very comforting.

After some nightly doses, I popped the empty bottle into the bin, telling my small niece, "That's the last of my cure."

Later on in the afternoon, the vicar called and said how pleased he was that I had recovered.

Just then, my niece appeared clutching the whisky bottle.

I was horrified when she proudly told the vicar, "That was Auntie's cure," and added, "but it's empty now."

GOING, GOING, GONE!

A few days ago my daughter-in-law went to an auction sale and took her small son, aged 2½ years, with her.

The auctioneer started with an item at £5 — then somebody bid £10.

The next bid was a loud shout of £100!

Everybody looked round in amazement and saw the bidder being hurriedly propelled from the room by a young mother with an extremely red face.

RAG DOLL!

I set off for my friend's wedding feeling rather smart in my new pink suit and navy-blue hat.

I parked the car and hurried into a shop in town to buy some confetti.

On my way out a small boy shouted: "Hey, are you in the parade, lady?"

It was Sheffield University Rag Day!!!

CHILDREN CROSSING!

We were preparing to emigrate to New Zealand and my husband was trying to make the trip as exciting as possible for my small daughter. He traced our proposed route on an atlas for her.

"Look," he said, pointing with his pen, "when we get to the Indian Ocean we will be very close to India. That's where your little friend at school comes from and just look how far she travelled from India to go to school in England."

"Gosh," exclaimed our six-year-old, obviously impressed, "and she's never late!"

ADULT'S CHOICE!

We have always taught our young son that, in the matter of television viewing, everyone's choice must be considered. Before switching any programme on or off, we've told him that others in the room must be consulted.

However, he carried this simple courtesy a little too far the other day when watching a children's programme.

Getting up to switch it off he said, "This is too babyish for me," then paused and added, "unless you want to see it, of course, Dad!"

TOEING THE LINE!

When I was reading "Uncle Tom's Cabin," to the children, I explained about the book and added — "It was written by Harriet Beecher Stowe."

The youngest one piped up — "There's a man on the telly who does funny things with his toes, but I don't think he could write a book with them!"

◀p136
I paused for breath, all the time trying to keep it steady.
He was still staring at the cottage, seeming not to have heard me. "Let's go and have a closer look. There used to be a pump in my grandfather's day."
"It's still there." I took his proffered help without embarrassment now. Strange how much easier a relationship was when there was open enmity to cushion it. "It's your grandfather's cottage?"
"Yes. He was hedger and ditcher for old Squire Langston at the big house. I came here in the summer sometimes. We used to drink cold milkless tea under a haystack and eat cheese and onion sandwiches." I thought suddenly — and with pleasure — he'd never tell that to Jackie.
We walked round the cottage without any of the house agent's optimism. He was silent again, remembering, I suppose. In the kitchen he took out a penknife and scratched at the limed brick. In the living-room he pushed the knife through the rose-strewn wallpaper and deep into the plaster and then picked away at the hole like a dentist at a rotten tooth. Plaster snowed on to the floorboards.
He noticed me. "You really want to live in this place?"
"I want it more than anything else in the world," I said simply.
"You're not going to doidy it up? Bathroom? Sun parlour? Thatch?"
"I couldn't if I wanted to." I thought about it, looking around me. "No, I wouldn't anyway. This is what I need. Ordinary, physical difficulties. No complications."
"It'll be complicated enough getting a modern coalman to deliver down here."
It was so near my own first misgiving that I smiled. "I can fetch my own in those plastic bags."
He said tersely, "They used to deliver logs from the big house."
It was as good as acceptance. I held my breath, but he said no more and after a while we trailed outside and got back into the car.

IT was past lunchtime, but we went through the village without stopping and the trip back seemed over much too quickly. When we were in the underground garage of the office block, he sat where he was, staring into the gloomy distances until the feeling of wind and movement had gone and we were reorientated.
When I began undoing Jackie's scarf he turned to face me.
"D'you want to tell me about it?" he asked — abruptly as if he hoped I didn't.
My mind whirled. I had been thinking entirely of the cottage.
"Tell you?" I sounded stupid.
He said patiently: "Start at the root of it all. Why did you divorce your husband?"
I started to gasp, it's none of your business. But I didn't. Nobody had ever asked me that before. Everyone who knew me, knew that Brian had gone off with Suzanne and that was that. People who met me afterwards assumed the same thing. But no-one had asked me.
I said very slowly and carefully, "Because he wanted me to."
"And that was enough?" He was direct, ruthless.
I thought again. Yes, that had been enough. I had known about Suzanne for some time, hoped that by keeping the lamp alight Brian

would come back to me. Immediately he asked for his freedom my love had started to die. There had been incredulity at first, deep hurt, self-pity. But love had died.

"Yes. That was enough."

His smile was at once relieved and congratulatory. But there was one more probing question. "You don't blame him?"

Oh, yes! I'd blamed Brian. Up until this minute when self-pity had evaporated in the blinding white light of truth, I'd blamed him for every frustrating miserable moment that had happened in the last three years. But how could I blame him now? I hadn't tried to keep him, I hadn't even talked to him about our marriage. My interest had gone when he announced that his had.

I said in a low voice, "I did blame him. Not now."

Bruce Kershaw became brisk, perhaps embarrassed. "Good girl. That's fine then." He leapt out of the car and helped me out. "I must leave you. I've some afternoon appointments. The agent has the name of your solicitors, I assume?"

I swallowed. "Yes."

"Then you'll be hearing from me. Goodbye."

He gripped my hand and turned away. I wanted to thank him.

"I'm so glad . . ." I began.

He turned, his face old-young and somehow suave in the uncertain light of the garage. "Yes?"

Courage went. "So glad the house agent will be getting his commission," I finished lamely.

IN spite of Christmas coming, the weeks went slowly after that. I made a few transactions — the solicitor called it realising my assets — visited the bank manager in between typing, seeing Dennis and pacifying my father on the telephone.

There had been no way of stopping him from viewing the cottage, and he and Mother were horrified. They communicated their depression to Dennis, who referred to Bruce Kershaw as "that property swindler."

But I didn't hear from Kershaw at all and neither did my solicitor. By the beginning of the holiday my nerve ends were showing. I was remembering that we hadn't clinched the sale even verbally. Worse still — in retrospect — he hadn't offered me lunch.

I took Dennis to Mother-in-law's on Christmas Eve. We had decided it would be nice if he spent two or three days with his father and I thought it would prove, to myself anyway, that there was no more animosity in me. I kept everything very matter-of-fact, but it was hard to fight off the sudden rush of self-pity as I took my leave of Dennis. I turned the car across country and drove to the cottage.

The short day had faded into night as I bumped down the lane. I was tired, cold and depressed. The sight of the concrete mixer outside the gate and the builder's lorry parked on the wallflowers crystallised the feeling of doom I had had for three weeks.

I pulled the handbrake on very slowly and switched off the engine, but no deep silence settled around me. Hammering and sawing came from behind the windows. The cottage was evidently being "doidied up."

There was no need for me to investigate, but I went inside anyway.

The flagged floor was cork tiled and the old brick walls were lined with pine planks. In the living-room two men toiled over a granite fireplace, a new window stood ready beneath the old leaded one, the roses had gone from the walls and the plaster was new and pink. The men looked up enquiringly.

"It looks . . . nice," I said feebly.

The older man shook his head, commiserating. " 'S not for sale, lady. Country retreat for one of the property magnates."

CHRISTMAS was quiet without Dennis. He telephoned twice; in the morning to tell me what Granny and Dad and Suzanne had given him; in the evening because he had forgotten to say thank you for my presents in the morning.

"Are you OK, Mum?" he asked after the third lot of pips.

It was hard for him to ask whether I was missing him. "Fine. Quiet though." It was harder still for me to tell him I was missing him, like thrusting the responsibility for my happiness on to his shoulders.

He caught on, though. "Just think, Mum. Next year we'll be in our own cottage and people will come to see us." It was so much what I wanted him to feel that, like a fool, I started to cry.

He went on unknowingly: "Dad says I can choose what to do tomorrow. I'll get him to drive us to the cottage and show everyone round a bit."

I started to tell him not to. Then I thought, why not, let him have his little hour of glory.

Three weeks later when Dennis was back at school I had a letter from the solicitor asking me if I could call. It was exactly two months since Bruce Kershaw had taken me to the cottage.

The solicitor — a friend of my father's who had guided me protectively through the divorce and treated me like an invalid — greeted me with rubbing hands and a pleased smile.

"You were wrong about that little place of yours, Sarah. He intends to sell to you, all right. I received the contract this morning, signed by him and enclosing an architect's certificate, so as I have already carried out the searches, it only needs your signature, my dear, and the place is yours."

I stared at him without immediate understanding. In my mind I had given the cottage up on Christmas Eve and had already started telling the family that I thought it was too far out.

"The price?" I stammered. He would want 18 thousand at least now.

"Fifteen thousand. As you agreed with him verbally."

"But I told you — he was tearing the inside right out . . ."

He put on his bedside manner. "Nevertheless. Come and look at the contract." I looked. It was true. The cottage was mine but for my signature. "Here's a pen, my dear." It was a mock quill. I stared at it.

"No . . ." I actually took the pen and poised it over the contract. Then I shook my head. "No. Not now. It's not my cottage now."

Bruce Kershaw telephoned the flat three days later. He was curt and to the point. "What's the big idea?"

He barked with unamused laughter. "You told me you liked it. You wanted to live in it more than anything else in the world. You *did*, didn't you?"

"I did. Oh, I did."

"Well? What's changed you?"

"I haven't changed. The cottage has changed."

"Oh, you've seen it." He blustered, "Don't you like it?"

"I love it. You have very good taste."

"Well then, what the devil's the matter, woman?"

"It's yours, of course."

"Rubbish! I planned it with you in mind. I'd have made the second bedroom into a bathroom but I knew you'd want it for your son. And I'd have had central heating, but I knew you needed a grate."

I couldn't resist it. "Why?" I asked curiously.

"To keep the home fire burning, naturally. Look here, Sarah, don't be stand-offish about it, I'll send the contract back, shall I?"

I wished he hadn't called me Sarah. It reminded me of Jackie and all the other shadowy, leggy blondes who had sat in his open car. It reminded me of Suzanne.

I said primly, "I've managed up till now without any charity, Mr Kershaw. Thank you very much but . . ."

"Shut up, woman!" he shouted, irritably. "Don't talk nonsense. Get your coat on. I'm coming round. We'll go down to the cottage again and you'll see what I mean. The place fits you like a shoe and if you want to give me twice its market price, then go ahead."

The phone was dead in my hand.

I had no intention of going with him, yet I was suddenly light-hearted. There was no escaping the fact that he was the only person I had felt easy with since Brian. And though at first this might have been simply because I thought him despicable, I knew now I did not despise him. But there was still Jackie, and I couldn't afford to let myself be hurt all over again in exactly the same way.

Yet when he came, my eyes were glad to look on him and they remembered him well, though we had met only once before. My ears remembered his voice, too. I thought: how can a trip to the country matter? When he silently took my old coat — not the fur one — off a peg in my little hall and held it out for me, I slipped my arms into it and smiled acceptance.

"Bring a scarf," he said quietly. "I've returned Jackie's."

WE drove without speaking again, and as we went through the village it started to snow. The cottage looked a picture, encased in grey sky like a glass ball, newly painted, the gate re-hung.

Bruce Kershaw clipped a cover over the car and we went inside. It was just right. He hadn't done too much or too little. It was still a farm labourer's cottage, but maybe he'd had a little win on the pools. And the grate was laid with apple logs.

Bruce squatted down and put a match to the paper. The snow had melted on his hair into pearly drops and in spite of his city suit he looked perfectly at home here. The boy who had spent summers with his grandfather drinking cold tea and eating cheese and onion sandwiches.

"Well?" He was looking up at me.

"It's . . ." I waved my hands. "It's lovely. It really is. I congratulate you. I'm sure your grandfather would be pleased."

He flushed with pleasure. "He wouldn't, actually. He was a stick in the mud, literally. But he'd like it for you."

It was my turn to colour; it was such a nice thing to say. I knew I didn't dare take this house now. It would be a bond between us, it would give him the power to step beneath my guard.

"I know why you won't have it, Sarah," he said in that direct way of his, but gently. "Don't you think you're being selfish? Like that snail we talked of? Now you think this place won't give you the protection you need, you're looking for another shell?"

"You mean, I should think of Dennis?" I said in a low voice. "I am doing that. How can I give him any security if I'm . . . vulnerable?"

"I wasn't thinking of Dennis."

He paused, then took a deep breath. "Sarah, listen. There was once a very foolish, conceited young man who imagined he was some kind of Prince Charming looking for his Cinderella. He played the field.

"He forgot she would come in disguise, and anyway he had no glass slipper. Then he found he had something better than a slipper. He had a tumble-down cottage that would look a mess to anyone but the real Cinderella.

"Well, he found her all right, but she would keep rushing away thinking it was midnight all the time. So he decided not to rush her. He'd let her wear the slipper until she got used to it. Until she got used to . . . Prince Charming. And then they could see. Just see what happened, Sarah. That's all."

There was a long silence. The snow brushed the window persuasively and the fire hissed and spat. Eventually I took out my handkerchief and blew my nose. He turned swiftly and I was terrified he might hold me or even pat my shoulder. He did neither, just stared right at my red face and my old coat and nodded, smiling with relief.

Then he said, "There's a kettle outside and the workmen left tea and sugar. Would you like to try some of Grandfather's milkless variety?"

Still I objected. "The fire will take ages to boil anything. Those logs are awfully damp."

"You wanted the ordinary domestic discomforts, remember." He still smiled and he looked so happy . . . so frighteningly happy. And I knew that already I was vulnerable because of his vulnerability.

"We're in no hurry, Sarah. We've waited a long time already and we're not going to spoil a decent pot of tea because we couldn't wait for the kettle to boil. Are we?"

I had to laugh. There was nothing else for it. We would simply have to wait to see if those damp logs could ever boil a kettle.

Of course, the water wasn't turned on, so we went out to the pump, and as it regurgitated water in great gulps, protesting, but doing its job as it always had, it seemed like a good omen.

Yes, the cottage was going to fit — just as comfortably as any old glass slipper.

* **THE END** *

The Wedding Jest!

A quiet wedding at home with a few friends — that's what we decided. Would someone please tell me where we went wrong?

By MRS D. LONGHURST

MANY words have been written and spoken upon the status of the father of the bride.

He is commonly supposed to be a shadowy figure, very much in the background, cheque book in hand — useful mainly for getting the bride to the church on time, to the altar without mishap, and for making, with much stuttering and hesitation, the traditional speech.

After that, his duties over, he sinks into oblivion. After all, isn't this the

REVENGE IS SWEET!

I was standing in the check-out queue at the library, when I heard the woman in front of me say to the librarian, "Twenty years married and he told me this morning I couldn't cook. I'll show him."

She marched out with a huge cookery book under her arm.

Two minutes later she was back.

"To heck with him," she said. "Why should bother," and handed the book back!

bride's day? And, after the bride, isn't the most important and powerful figure the mother of the bride?

This is what I thought. But, mothers of brides-to-be, please take note — there is no greater fallacy!

I doubt if my presence at the church had any effect on anyone. I crept down the aisle, unnoticed and unsung. Afterwards, by pressing forward with all my strength, I did manage to get in one or two of the photographs.

I flew along after my husband and the bridegroom's parents in order to get a lift home to the reception. (If I hadn't done just that, I am convinced I would have had to hoof it).

On arriving home I organised the traditional reception committee of bride's parents, bridegroom's parents, bride and 'groom, in that order, to welcome all the guests.

Everyone was primed beforehand and knew what they had to do.

In effect, what happened was quite the opposite. I found myself fighting through the millng crowd to get to my own front door, and once there I stood with a fixed grin, prepared to shake everyone by the hand.

My husband had forsaken his duty and was outside laughing and joking with the guests, while the bridegroom's mother, whom I managed to catch hold of en route, was placed at a vantage point opposite me on the stairs.

From there she was able to bend forward at intervals in the crush and shake hands with those she knew or pat others on the head.

I wasn't so lucky. Apart from the faithful few who still insisted I was the bride's mother and therefore a "very important person," I was looked upon as a piece of furniture, and by others, as a faithful family retainer. Whenever I appeared after that, I was assailed with requests for "a nice cup of tea" or "find my husband for me, dear."

IT all started about 18 months ago, when my daughter decided she would like a "quiet" wedding at home. We wholeheartedly agreed and began planning along those lines.

I said I would make the bridal dress and the cake. Alison, in a fit of enthusiasm, went out one day, bought material for bridesmaids' dresses and made them both within a week.

Needless to say, as the wedding day approached, both bridesmaids, being in their early teens, had sprouted out in all directions and the dresses had to be taken apart and made up all over again.

About this time Alison decided she would order wedding invitations and asked her fiancé Alan for the list of his relations and friends.

This list in itself was daunting enough, but when Alan announced that he would have to invite his football club, plus their girlfriends as well, I thought to myself — in for a penny, in for a pound.

We started rounding up our friends and relations — quite a sizeable number. I never before realised we had so many.

ABOUT this time, friends in the neighbourhood suddenly awakened to the fact that there was to be a wedding in the near future, and I was besieged on all sides by offers of help, food, flowers, and requests for wedding-present lists.

I would like to say here and now that I am still overwhelmed by the help given on all sides. Indeed, but for it, I think I should have gone under.

The thought of entertaining 70 guests at home was in itself daunting enough, but when the acceptances began to flow in, we realised that all the "unexpected" would also be attending.

I must confess I did consider retiring quietly to the nearest mental home to have a long nervous breakdown.

THE making of the cake was a great event — it was a family occasion — everyone mucking in and lending a hand: blanching almonds; chopping almonds; cleaning fruit; weighing, measuring, mixing — everything had to be just right.

Then came the snag. How was I going to bake two tiers in the same oven at the same time? Or, alternatively, would it be all right to bake one on one day and one the next, or should I stay up all night?

In the end I housed one tier in my cooker and at the same time my friend down the road baked the other one in hers.

I wonder how many wedding cakes have been baked by this method — the top tier by gas and the bottom one by electricity!

The next stage provided no difficulties, the almond paste went on smoothly, just as it should, and I was gaining in confidence all the time.

Why, when the time came, I would even put on the final coat of icing myself and everyone would think the whole thing had been carried out by a professional.

The wedding was by now very near and I had found plenty to do to occupy my time.

Each day I thought to myself, I must ice the cake. But each day passed and the cake still reposed on my chest of drawers in the bedroom in its casing of almond paste and polythene.

Daily, I became more and more frustrated and eventually, in desperation, shelving all other duties, I brought the wretched cake downstairs and put it on the table, grimly determined to do or die in the attempt.

It was quite the wrong thing to do. It was late in the evening, I was tired, the light was bad, and the icing simply would not go on smoothly. The more I tried, the worse it looked.

Next morning I peered at it critically but it looked no better — in fact, it seemed to me to look a great deal worse.

I sent out an SOS to my pal down the road, and to do her justice, she did not comment on the imperfect state of the coat of icing.

She probably felt that by now I was so near nervous exhaustion that the slightest remark by her might send me over the edge.

She took over, and in no time at all, the two tiers were covered with marvellous decorations.

Crowned with a truly handsome centrepiece of lily-of-the-valley, it was a sight for sore eyes. Another obstacle surmounted.

ON the evening before the wedding the house was filled with friends who came pouring in to help get the buffet ready for the Great Day.

I eventually coaxed the bride into a hot bath, ironed her wedding dress, rearranged the furniture, cleaned the carpet and tidied everything in readiness. Then I hopped into bed for a few hours of sleep to restore my flagging strength.

I gave the bride her traditional breakfast in bed. Far from being wan and pale and a little tremulous, she sat up and demanded a fried egg sandwich!

But thank goodness something made her for once want to get dressed early. She must have had a premonition.

About an hour beforehand, I got her into her wedding dress. It looked a dream, in white satin, with blue smocking — simple but dignified.

I felt justifiably proud. I had done a good job. Now came the crowning moment.

She stepped into it and I pulled the zip — all 22 inches of it. To my horror it pulled apart from stem to stern!

Whichever way I pulled it, it just parted company with the dress! How could the bride go to meet her bridegroom with a 22-inch gap in the back of her dress!

I felt a moment of sheer panic. The bride took a good strong drink and I yelled for my sister-in-law. She used to be a dressmaker and she would know what to do. It was a case of all hands to the pump — a real EMERGENCY!

I'll never know how that next half-hour passed. People kept peeping in the door to be shooed away. My brother would not be kept away, and insisted upon coming in and embracing all and sundry.

Steadily we sewed the bride into her wedding dress. It was a close shave, but we got her sewn in with about 20 minutes to spare, by which time I was reduced to a mass of trembling nerves.

At last the taxis arrived and the last thing I remember doing before getting into the car was to check that I had a clean hankie to cry into.

I'M afraid I can't tell you much about the ceremony. I remember hearing the first notes of the "Wedding March" boom out on the organ, and when I looked round there was Dad, looking very smart, upright and dependable, with the bride on his arm, just rounding the corner to meet the bridegroom and the minister.

From then on I could think of nothing but that 22-inch zip. I focused my eye on the bride's back as if to dare the stitching to give way.

At any moment I was quite sure I should hear an ominous rip and no-one will ever know the agonies I endured during that ceremony.

Once the service was over and we were proceeding to the vestry, the full significance hit me. My eldest daughter had been transformed into a married woman before my very eyes and I hadn't shed a single tear!

Well, it's all over now, but I have learned two important facts about weddings during these past few months.

Firstly, however long and hard we save, there will never be enough money for the next one. There are always those unexpected, last-minute expenses one never caters for.

And, secondly, and most important of all — there is no such thing as a "quiet wedding!"

The End.

THE RIGHT THING TO DO

Complete Story by MARY E. KNOWLES

At the time, it had seemed to her a simple decision to make. Only later did she learn just how important it proved to those she loved.

WHEN Anne Delaney reached the bank, there were already long lines of people waiting before the four tellers' cages. Her dark eyes quickly counted each line and she chose the one closest because there were two people less. She told the boys: "Sit over there on those chairs against the wall."

Eddie said, "But, Mum, it's such a long queue." He looked up at her, his blue eyes and the shock of red hair that had escaped his woollen helmet making him look so like his father that she had a sudden pain inside sharper than the day Bert died.

"Hurry up, Mummy, hurry up," Graham said. "I'm tired."

"I know, darling." This was Graham's first day out since he had measles, and his four-year-old face was thin, some of the baby roundness gone.

There had been the long wait for the bus in the cold, and they still had to walk to the other end of town to buy shoes at the dividend store.

She bent down. "When Miss King drives us home maybe she will stop at the Corner Café, if her father isn't too tired."

May King was her neighbour. She had told Anne, "I have to take Dad to the doctor. If you're at the store when we get out, I'll drive you home." This would be a great relief with the weather so bad.

"You can each have a treat later," she told the boys.

They hugged her knees. "Oh, boy! Gosh, thanks, Mum." Then Eddie said, "Come on, Graham."

She watched them as they ran for a chair and sat stiffly on the edge. They were such wonderful boys. When Bert died eight months ago, 10-year-old Eddie had taken over as man of the house. He called for Graham at the nursery every day, and, when Anne got home from the office, the table was set for dinner and the kettle was boiling so she could have a cup of coffee.

Anne had no money to spare for treats, but the boys had earned it. As she moved slowly along with the queue, she looked at her weekly pay cheque, knowing where each penny of it was going.

She had a good future at the law office, and she was going to evening classes to learn shorthand, but at the moment they lived from pay day to pay day with very little left over. And this pay cheque was smaller, because she had had to stay off work for four days to take care of Graham.

She finally reached the teller's window. The middle-aged teller had sparse hair and his mouth turned down at the corners. He took her cheque, asked grouchily for identification, then, satisfied, counted out notes, then rechecked and counted again. He looked as if his mind were on something else. Then he said shortly, "Next!"

Anne picked up the money and put it carefully in her purse. "All right, boys," she called.

OUTSIDE, it was snowing. She knelt, buttoned Graham's jacket to the top, fastened Eddie's cap under his chin and pulled her knitted hat down over her fair hair.

They couldn't walk the length of the High Street in this! Maybe she should go to Anderson's shoe shop. She could telephone May at the doctor's surgery to meet them there.

Then she remembered that the money she saved at the store sale would buy the boys each two pairs of warm socks. And the shoes were good. But it was self-service and the stock was usually last year's rejects.

"Come on," she said. "Let's go."

Eddie took hold of her jacket, Graham clung to her hand, and, heads down, they headed into the snow. The going was rough, and 15 minutes later, Anne pulled them into a doorway. Graham was crying. "I'm cold, Mummy. Let's go home. I don't want new shoes."

She was cold, too. Her car coat had been meant for driving in a warm car. She saw their bus coming and almost weakened, then remembered that it would be a week before she could bring the boys from the suburbs where they lived into the city, and their shoes would not last another week.

"We can get through this," she said gaily. "Let's pretend we are on our way to the North Pole, and the first one who gets there can put up the Union Jack and . . ."

"And the enemy is going to try to beat us there!" The boys entered into the fantasy and they covered the remaining distance in record time. Then they were in the warmth of the shoe shop, and the boys were sitting on chairs, and she was hunting through the racks of shoes.

She was in luck and found a sturdy, thick-soled pair of shoes for each

EARLY START!

Newly married, we found ourselves oversleeping the alarm several times a week, resulting in my husband being late for work.

Needless to say, it was drummed into me that we simply must get up as soon as the alarm rings.

The following day, I bounced out of bed, quickly made a pot of tea and cooked breakfast. I then took everything into the bedroom and gave my tired husband a good shake, saying: "Wake up, wake up, it's nearly . . . (I turned to look at the clock) . . . it's nearly, er — 3 o'clock!"

of them. She wanted to buy a pair of overshoes to protect them, but that would have to wait until next month.

It was when she went to pay the assistant that she found the extra 20 pounds. While the assistant was wrapping the shoes, she sat down and counted her money.

The shoes were her only purchase, and she'd had only small change to begin with. She remembered how absent minded the teller had been. He had given her 20 pounds too much!

"What's the matter, Anne?"

She looked up and May King was standing there, a blue scarf tied over her grey hair.

"I have twenty pounds more than I should have," Anne said.

"Good for you." May laughed shortly. May had been a good neighbour to Anne. She had been so kind when Graham was sick, sitting with him while Anne went shopping, but there was a streak of hardness in her.

May had never married. She talked constantly of her great romance with a Fred Dallas. She'd had to turn him down because her mother had a stroke and none of the other brothers and sisters would take the responsibility. And now her eighty-year-old father had to be taken care of.

"But, of course, I can't keep it, May," she said.

"Why not? The bank has a vault full of twenty-pound notes and you certainly can use it."

That was true. Twenty pounds would buy many things. It would buy the overshoes, or she could give Mr Swanson, the grocer, something extra. He had given them credit for a whole year while Bert was ill, and had waited so patiently for his money. He had four small children. He could use 20 pounds, and the bank certainly did have a vault full of money.

And then, suddenly, she was a little girl and Mother was telling her: "Honesty above all, Anne. Don't take as much as a straight pin that doesn't belong to you."

"Oh, I couldn't keep it, May!"

"Why not?" May asked.

"Because it's not mine, and keeping it would be stealing." She suddenly remembered how cross the teller had been. Maybe he had a reason, a very sick wife or a mortgage payment overdue. "The teller would have to pay the money out of his own pocket."

"Well, that's his tough luck," May said. "He's paid to be accurate."

Anne shook her head. "I can't keep it. I've got to take it back."

"Suit yourself." May shrugged her shoulders. "But I can't wait. Dad's in the car and he's hungry and cross as a bear. But let me tell you, if I hadn't been such a soft-headed fool . . ."

She went on and on, telling the story she had told so many times before, how she had taken care of her sick parents and Ed and Jack and Shirley had just turned their backs on her, and so Fred had married another girl . . .

Anne looked after her neighbour as she walked out of the store, feeling sorry for her. May's father had told Anne, "Fred was never in love with her. She just imagined it, and she has ruined her life thinking she missed her big chance."

"Aren't we going with her?" Eddie asked.

"No, son. I have to go back to the bank."

Graham began to cry. "I want a treat."

"You'll get your treat, darling," she said. "I promise you."

"Don't cry now, Graham!" Eddie said sternly, but he, too, looked regretfully after May's plump figure.

THE long walk back to the bank was cold and wet, the wind had risen and the icy pellets of snow peppered their faces, but they finally reached the bank. There was, thank goodness, no queue at the middle-aged teller's window and she walked right up to him.

She saw the nameplate: *Thomas Eddrington.* "Mr Eddrington," she said, "when you cashed my cheque you made a mistake. You . . ."

Early Morning Blues

I WOULD be the last person to claim that I am of the stuff champion early-risers are made of. Indeed, to be perfectly honest about it I am never likely to win medals for any ability to rise and greet the dawn cheerfully and willingly.

But — and it pains me to admit it — of late I have been awakening regularly at the ungodly hour of six a.m.

I am not a free agent in the matter. I am the victim of a ruthless, selfish, demanding sadist . . . one against whom I am defenceless.

I refer to my cat.

Why she should decide that six o'clock in the morning is my appointed hour for rising, I just don't know.

I do know that every morning at that hour, she arrives, with a thump, on me as I lie in bed, purring away happily as she wakens me with muted cries and light taps of her paw.

I have, of course, tried to outwit her by keeping the bedroom door firmly shut. It doesn't help. I can't sleep through continual scratching at the other side of the door, to say nothing of the most heart-rending, plaintive cries which demand to know why I have done such a thing to her!

So it goes on — and no doubt will go on until my cat's inbuilt alarm clock gets back to the proper regular hour at which I do get up.

But in the meantime —!

"You should always count your money before you leave the window." He shrugged his shoulders.

She almost turned on her heel and stalked out. May was right. It was his headache, not hers. Her voice shook. "You gave me twenty pounds too much."

"Oh . . ." His face turned red. He hastily counted through the notes in the drawer, compared the amount with figures on a sheet of paper. "Yes, I am twenty short." But he didn't thank her. He almost snatched the note from her hand.

Anne turned slowly and looked at her tired, patient little boys. "Now," she said with a brightness she did not feel, "now for that treat."

"I'd like a hamburger," Eddie said.

"With chips," Graham begged.

In the Corner Café, Anne ordered only coffee for herself, but she couldn't even drink that because she was suddenly nauseated, remembering the way the teller had behaved. He could have said, "Thank you." Maybe May was right and she was a fool.

WHEN they arrived home it was almost dark. She made hot chocolate for the boys, read to them, and finally they were in bed. There was a knock at the door. It was May.

She held out a plate of freshly-baked cinnamon buns.

"Thought you might enjoy them," she said. Anne knew it was her way of apologising for not waiting to drive them home.

"Why, thank you so much," Anne said. "It's very kind of you."

May asked, "Did the teller say, 'Thank you, kind, honest lady?' "

"No." Disappointment and anger washed over Anne. "He behaved as if it were my fault."

"Was he a bald-headed man, sour looking?" May's eyes narrowed. "Thomas Eddrington?"

"Why, yes, that was his name."

May laughed. "And you dragged your little boys along the High Street through a blizzard to give him twenty pounds. Thomas Eddrington is a bachelor. He learned to play the stock market, how to invest his money. Why, he owns two buildings in town. He has his own house."

"Then why is he working in a bank?"

"Because he loves money. He likes to handle it, count it, earn more, even that small salary. Besides, he hasn't anything else to do." May added wryly, "He needs those twenty pounds like he needs another set of toes!

"Listen, Anne," May said. "You're all alone now, and you've got two boys to support. You have to be a bit more clever, a bit more ruthless, or you'll get stepped on. Believe me, Anne, I know. If only I'd told my brothers and sisters, 'Mother and Dad are your responsibility. I'm going to marry the man I love."

She patted Helen's shoulder. "Stop being a sucker," she said, a gentleness in her voice.

AFTER May had gone, Anne leaned against the closed door and cried quietly, tears sliding down her cheeks. She missed Bert's arms around her, because she was afraid of the responsibility of rearing her two sons, because the code by which she had been reared wasn't good any more. How could she teach them what was right when she didn't know what was right herself!

But most of all she cried because she was disillusioned. She had done the right thing, the honest thing, but it had turned out to be a foolish thing.

After a while she stopped crying and went through the automatic movements of finishing the dishes. She heard Graham cough. She went into the bedroom to comfort him.

Eddie was asleep, the blankets thrown off. She covered him, kissed him lightly on the forehead. He had left his light on. She walked over to turn it off and saw his "Captain's Log," as he called it, open on the table . . .

Bert had known he was dying. He had spent a lot of time talking to the boys. He had told Eddie, "Being a man is a big job, but it doesn't happen all at once. Each day you learn something that helps you when you are a man."

And he had given Eddie a large journal. "This is like a captain's log on a ship. Each night the captain writes what has happened during the day, and every night you must write down what you have learned during your day."

Towards the end Bert had told Anne, "I seem to talk in platitudes: 'Good is rewarded — As the twig is bent so the tree grows . . .' things like that. But there is so much I want to teach the boys, and there is so little time left. I don't know if I'm getting through to them."

Anne had never read Eddie's journal. She respected his privacy, but here it was open and her eyes skimmed lightly over what he had written. Systematically he had numbered his day's findings, writing in a careful, childish hand:

1. It takes a long time for the bus to come in winter.

2. New shoes make me feel taller.

3. The hamburger man liked cooking for us. He was happy we ate every bit.

Anne smiled fondly, surprised and pleased that Eddie had had the insight to know that the hamburger man enjoyed watching them eat his cooking.

And then she read No. 4 and for a moment the words blurred through her tears. She brushed them away and read again, going sick inside, thinking back to the moment when she had almost agreed with May, unaware that all she did and said was being taken as gospel because she said and did it.

No. 4, Eddie had written. *If you have something that belongs to someone, take it back, even if you have to walk a mile and a half and it's snowing and your boys are crying. Because it doesn't belong to you and you have to give it back, even if somebody else says keep it, don't be a sucker.* And he had added, capitalising each word, *"Honesty Is The Best Policy."*

"Amen," Anne said softly. She closed the journal and walked out of the bedroom, her head held high as befitted one who had been tried and not been found wanting.

*** THE END ***

SPOT THE DIFFERENCE!

My grandfather used to tell this story, which is quite true.

He has an identical twin, but was neither born on the same day, week, month nor year, as his brother.

Grandad was born on a Saturday which was Hogmanay, but his brother was born after midnight on a New Year's morning which was Sunday!

SOLUTION TO CROSSWORD

Across — 2 Try, 4 Stall, 5 Peals, 6 Ass, 8 Gas, 10 Days, 13 Akin, 15 Hour, 16 Told, 17 Panto, 19 Noose, 21 Gay, 22 Sample, 24 Manger, 27 Band, 28 Tense, 30 Rice, 31 Brotherly, 34 Applaud, 35 Tonsure.

Down — 1 Fir, 2 Tatters, 3 Yule Log, 7 Sky, 9 Ark, 11 Adorn, 12 Scrooge, 13 Antonym, 14 Igloo, 18 Aimed, 20 Sugar, 22 Sea, 23 Lit, 25 Ace, 26 Roc, 29 Nicholas, 32 Roast, 33 Ladle.

Special Long Complete Story by ISOBEL STEWART

WHEN ALL THE TEARS ARE SHED

There was no easy answer to their problem. All they could do was draw a little closer together and face whatever the future might bring.

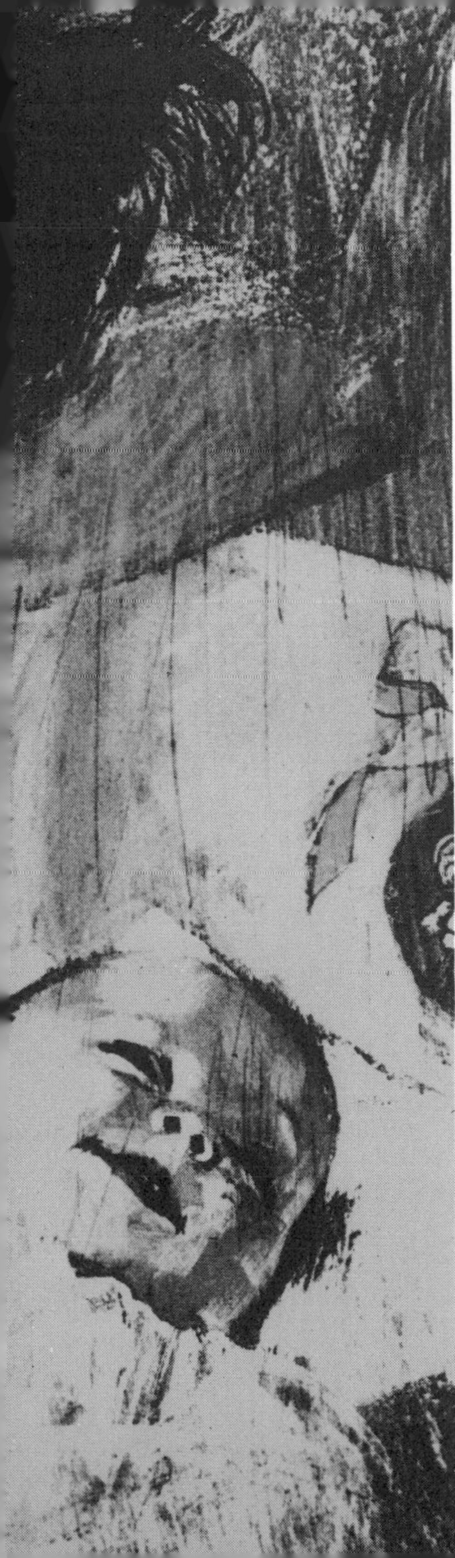

WHEN it was all over, Diane came home.

They went to collect her, driving through the night, neither of them saying much. Marion knew that James, too, was wondering how it would be with Diane, wondering what these last long and lonely months would have done to their daughter.

All the 17 years of Diane's life stretched behind them, but yet Marion found she could capture only fleeting memories of Diane before all this. Sitting on the stairs as she answered the telephone, her small face rapt under the long straight hair. Cross-legged in front of the fire, solemnly and seriously painting her toenails. Running out to meet the boy, her short skirt swinging, her eyes wide with the wonder of being 17, being in love, just being alive.

And farther back, too. Diane on her trike in the quiet street, her eyes closed blissfully, her small face lifted to the sunshine.

So many memories. And yet nothing was real any more, because of these last months. Since that morning when she'd found out.

That was real enough even now, eight months later. Even thinking of it, Marion felt all the colour leave her face, felt her hands once again cold and clammy. She had known right away, as she stood in the bathroom and faced Diane, her face still white from the sudden sickness which had overwhelmed her. And Diane had known, too, looking back at her mother.

"Don't, love," James said gently, his hand covering hers for a moment. "It's all over."

Yes, Marion thought tiredly, it's all over. The baby has already gone to his new parents and there are only the final papers to sign.

Diane was waiting for them, sitting beside her suitcase, her hands folded. The first thing Marion saw was her hair.

"Your hair, Di — you've had it cut."

The girl smiled.

"You've always wanted me to have it cut, Mum. They said it would be easier, so I had it cut."

Her long, heavy hair had been Diane's pride and joy. And in spite of the times she'd said it would be better short, suddenly and surprisingly Marion wished she could have seen Diane lift one hand and flick her hair behind her ear.

Awkwardly, not saying much, James greeted his daughter. Then, while he went to see the matron, Marion took Diane's case out to the car, and they got in. There was so much Marion wanted to say.

"Di," she said at last, uncertainly. "Are you — all right?"

"Yes, thank you, Mummy." It was Diane's voice, and yet . . . But how could I expect her not to have changed, Marion thought, half angrily. A girl can't go through this and still be the same. Not a girl like Diane.

IT was a long journey home, long and tiring. The road was strange to James, and he concentrated on his driving. Once, Diane asked about her elder sister, Margaret. Marion said she was much better now, although she still had to be careful.

"These chest things," she finished, vaguely. It didn't seem necessary for Diane to know just how worried they'd all been. Margaret, newly married, was clear now of the possibility of treatment in a hospital, but for months to come she'd still be under medical supervision. And there could be no question of a child for some time.

"Are she and Bill still with you?" Diane asked, but Marion told her that they had gone back to their own little flat, which they had had to leave when Margaret needed constant nursing.

It was late when they got home, and Marion felt tired, her head aching. The house was cold and she hurried around turning on heaters, putting the kettle on, glad of something to do. As she set out cups and made tea, Diane followed her around, as if, Marion thought helplessly, she was a visitor. As if this wasn't her home.

She said this to James later, when they were in bed, trying to keep her voice steady as she told him.

"Give her time, Marion. Don't rush her."

It wasn't easy to keep her voice from shaking.

"I thought it would be all right when we got her home," she whispered.

"All right? Our problems are only starting now," James said.

"Is she going on to university?" James asked. "If she does, are we going to let her go away from home? And if she doesn't, what is she going to do? All right, we tell ourselves no-one knows, but how sure can we be? A girl leaving school suddenly, halfway through her last year . . ."

But that wasn't what I meant, Marion thought, shaken. These are all — outside things, things we can solve as we come to them. I meant Diane herself. Because if she isn't all right herself, then — then nothing else will be. And I don't think she is, I don't see how she can be, although somehow I thought she would.

In the early days of having Diane home again, the strange feeling that she was a visitor, that she didn't really belong here, persisted. Marion found herself asking her daughter what she'd like for lunch, if she'd be all right left on her own for an hour. And the disturbing thing was that Diane, too, seemed conscious of this strangeness.

It came out in so many little ways — her apology for keeping her father waiting when she was washing her hair; her regular, undemanded help with housework, all the things she had done before only on sufferance, the way she listened when Marion or James talked to her, giving them her whole attention, her eyes never leaving their faces as she listened.

James said she had changed for the better. The whole thing, he said, dreadful as it was, seemed to have taught her such a lesson that they'd never have any trouble with her again.

"But we didn't ever have any trouble with her," Marion reminded him. And they hadn't. She had been, her mother thought now, a normal, high-spirited girl, sometimes disobedient, sometimes rebellious. But she hadn't been a problem teenager.

She'd grumbled about their rules, but she'd kept them. And if she did argue, or flare up, within half an hour she was apologising, her strong young arms hugging Marion, her long hair against her mother's face as she said she was sorry . . .

"No," James agreed. "So — why did it happen?"

We've been through it all so many times, Marion thought helplessly. Why did it happen — to a girl like Diane?

"It's so blasted unfair," James went on, and the controlled anger in his voice made her look at him as if he was a stranger, although she had heard him speak like this so often, since Diane went away. "He's off to university as if nothing had happened, and Diane . . ."

AT James' suggestion, Diane started a secretarial course, going to town every morning with her father, and coming home in the middle of the afternoon. When they asked her how she felt about university, she thanked them politely and said she didn't really think she wanted to go.

Gradually, Marion began to pick up the threads of her life again, to go to coffee mornings and even an occasional game of bridge.

But it wasn't easy. For as well as having Diane always on her mind, there was the constant guard, the ever-present danger of giving something away. For at the start, James had said that no-one must be told.

"All right," he'd said, his eyes dark and unhappy, "people will wonder. But if we stick to our story — that Diane's spending a few months with a distant cousin because she's a bit run down — then no-one can say anything. Just tell one person, though, Marion, and you might as well tell the whole town. It has to be this way, for Diane's sake."

Somehow, it had been easier not to say anything while Diane was away. There had been Margaret, too, the worry about her, the work of looking after her. And really, Marion thought now, there hadn't been much time for seeing even close friends.

But now Margaret was better, Diane was home, and sometimes she thought that what she wanted most in the world was to tell one person — Louise, probably — the whole story. They'd been friends for so long, and in the past months she had so often found Louise looking at her a little sadly, her blue-grey eyes questioning, waiting.

But she'd said nothing, though each time she and Louise were together she felt the constraint between them that had never been there before, in all the years of their friendship.

Because of that, she could understand how Diane felt when Elaine came. They, too, had been friends for a long time. Seeing Elaine at the door, her hair long and straight, her eyes bright the way Diane's used to be, Marion would have given anything to turn back the clock and have

Diane running down to meet her friend, her long hair flying.

"I think Di's out in the garden, Elaine. Go on up to her room."

When Elaine had gone up the stairs, Marion hurried through to the kitchen, where Diane was drying dishes.

"Elaine's here, Di. I'll finish these." She hesitated, and then, quickly, she said, "Di . . .. did you tell her anything before you — went away?"

All the colour left Diane's face, and she shook her head.

"Di . . . There's no need to say anything now, no-one need ever know. Your father — we told people you'd gone to stay with Aunt Helen because you were a bit run down."

Diane nodded. "I know, Mum — you said that was what you'd do."

"I just thought I'd remind you," she murmured, ill-at-ease. "Do you and Elaine want coffee?"

"Don't bother, Mum, we'll come and make it if we want," Diane replied. And then she added, quickly, "If that's all right?"

"Darling, of course it's all right," Marion said, not quite steadily. Tears pricked her eyes for the girl who'd once accepted her home and her parents so easily and naturally. Even thoughtlessly sometimes, Marion thought, but — that was how it should be.

IN half an hour Elaine came to say goodbye. Marion could see in her young face the same sadness and bewilderment that had been in Louise's.

"Can't get Di persuaded to do anything, Mrs Martin," Elaine said brightly, too brightly, Marion knew. "She doesn't want to come out for a coffee and she can't be bothered with a party tonight. I bet she met some fab fellow up north — that's why poor Steve got the brush-off. 'Bye, Mrs Martin — give me a ring, Di."

Then she was gone, and some of the brightness from the day went with her.

Marion glanced at Diane to see how she had taken the mention of Steve Ledgerwood, saw that she was looking after Elaine, watching the fair hair swinging along.

"Di, why don't you go to the party?" Marion suggested. "You might as well, you know — better fun than sitting in here with us."

But Diane only shook her head, her soft mouth set. And Marion was reminded of the time, months ago, when they'd asked her if she wanted to marry Steve Ledgerwood. Then, too, she'd shaken her head without saying anything. And Marion, knowing that her daughter's mind was completely made up, hadn't known whether to feel relieved or sorry.

"Mum," Diane said now, sitting down on one of the kitchen stools, "you didn't tell me Maragaret had been so ill. Elaine was telling me now — she said for a bit it looked as if she might have to go into hospital. Margaret didn't say anything herself, either, when she came to see me. When was this?"

Startled at the unexpected pinning-down, Marion found herself telling Diane that it had been a month after she went away.

"So you knew when you came up to see me?" Diane asked thoughtfully. Then she smiled, and Marion's heart gave an unexpected lift, for it was a real smile. "So you must have been worried about

Margaret, that time . . . and I thought . . ." She stopped speaking.

"What did you think, Di?" Marion asked gently.

Diane looked up to meet her mother's eyes. "I thought you were still angry and upset and — and disappointed. You were so quiet. But I suppose you were so worried about Margaret, you just — weren't really seeing me?"

"I suppose so," Marion agreed carefully. But she was thinking — I saw you, Diane, and my heart ached for you when I saw how you looked. You had been so small and slim before. I saw you, but — yes, I was worried about Margaret and worried about you, worried about so many things.

"I'm sorry, Diane," she said, her voice low. She didn't really know what she was apologising for.

"It's all right," Diane replied politely, and she went out of the kitchen.

SHE can't go on like this," Marion said to James that night. "She does nothing but go to her classes, and come home. She isn't even interested in new clothes.I said I thought she needed some new things and she just couldn't have cared less."

Then she was crying, her face buried in her hands. Crying softly and hopelessly, not wanting Diane to hear her. "James, why did it happen, where did we go wrong?"

Gently he took her hands away from her face, and she saw the same despair in his eyes that she felt herself.

"Darling, I don't know. I've asked myself that so often — we've gone over it again and again. And there isn't any answer. It just did happen, that's all there is to it." For a moment his face darkened. "I blame him, of course. A girl like Diane . . ."

There was some thought just round the corner of Marion's mind, something she just couldn't get hold of.

"James, you know something?" she said hesitantly. "I don't think we'll get anywhere wondering why it happened to a girl like Diane. We just have to accept that it did, in spite of us, in spite of Diane. It happened — and nothing can change that. We've got to stop looking backwards. Diane's got to start living again, and we've got to help her."

It was the barrier that seemed to have grown between Diane and herself that Marion found hardest to take. They'd always been close, closer than she and Margaret had been. But Margaret, even as a child, had always been far more self-sufficient and more self-confident than Diane, and always a little impatient with her young sister.

The impatience was still there, Marion found, when in desperation she went over to see Margaret one day and they talked about Diane.

"If there was just something I could do or say to help her," she murmured.

"Mum, you've done all anyone could — more, even," Margaret replied, and Marion looked at her elder daughter, a little surprised.

Margaret flushed. "You've always had this tendency to protect Diane too much. Now something's happened that you haven't been able to protect her from and she's had to face it on her own. Of course it's taking her a long time to get to grips with it. Let's face it, Mum, having

Beware Of The CATS

WE don't feel so good at the moment. We feel a little neglected, if you know what we mean. That's why we're resting. We think it is rather nice of you lot to have such charming snoozing baskets made especially for the likes of us. And don't think we're not truly appreciative merely because we would like to suggest that a little more padding and an electric blanket would be most welcome.

We trust you won't get needled at us if we continue such a subject so close to our purring hearts.

an illegitimate child when you're only seventeen isn't just the best start to life, and Diane knows it."

"You're — hard, Margaret," Marion said, not quite steadily. And she thought with sadness that there would be no help here for Diane.

Then she remembered how hard the last months had been for Margaret. She asked how the last check-up had gone.

Margaret shrugged. "Much the same — disease arrested, treatment continuing." Her eyes met her mother's. "No question of starting a family for quite a time."

Marion thought of all the obvious things she could say to Margaret — she was young, there was plenty of time, she was lucky not to have had to go into hospital — but in the end she said nothing, only covered Margaret's hand with her own. Margaret looked up at last, and her eyes were bright with tears.

"Thanks, Mum," she whispered shakily, trying to smile. "It always helps, just seeing you."

MARION was alone in the house the afternoon Steve Ledgerwood came. Hurriedly, she wiped her hands on her apron when she heard the front doorbell ring.

He was leaning against the door, the way he always used to. His hair was longer than ever, and his jeans tighter. He smiled, his easy, casual smile, full of friendliness, full of charm.

"Hi, Mrs Martin," he said easily. "I've just come home. Thought I'd look up and see Di."

Everything in Marion stiffened.

"How dare you come here!" she whispered, her lips stiff. "After all that's happened, how dare you — how dare you even mention Diane's name!"

Steve Ledgerwood straightened.

"Take it easy, Mrs Martin . . ."

"Take it easy!" Marion blazed. And then suddenly, frighteningly, it was all too much for her.

She turned away. "If you could see Diane, if you could see the way she is now . . ."

Surprisingly, his hand shot out and grasped her wrist hard. ▶p162

;ats, being truly superior, need all the ɿuisite comfort, all the rich indolent ury, and all the elegant trappings that ı lot can continue to produce. It's not :ing much, is it?

ıfter all, darn it, we cats don't ask much ɹre from you than some- where to sleep, nething to eat, and the odd gallon or ɔ to drink.

Vell, having said our little piece, we ık we'll go on guard duty, that is to say, t though our eyes will by shut, and our ıds might sink to our paws, and our tails will be curled around to keep out draughts, we shall actually be *alert* and *at the ready.*

Just let anything — be it Martian or human or any other kind of monster — come barging in around here, and we shall have him!

That's the way we work. Always on the go, we are. If we were to tell you just how great we really are, your head would simply reel, really it would.

We do wish you'd stop laughing at us. You'll only get a stitch in your side . . .

◀p160
"What's wrong with Diane?" he asked roughly. "They — they told me she was all right, they said she'd come back from — from up north, and she was at a business college. What's wrong with her?"

Startled, Marion looked up at him. And for the first time she really saw him. Not a man, but a bewildered, confused boy, who had tried to pretend to be light and casual about coming here to see Diane, tried to pretend everything was as it always had been before. Before Diane had his child, Marion thought, and with the thought came sudden clarity and an instinctive action.

"Come and have a cup of coffee, Steve," she said steadily. And she saw the last of his defences crumble away. He followed her through to the kitchen. And there, sitting at the table, she told him about Diane and how worried she was about her.

He stirred his coffee, not saying anything. Then, when she had finished, he looked up at her.

"Why didn't you let her marry me?" he asked, and Marion saw that in the long weary months he had done a lot of growing up himself.

"Because she didn't want to," she told him. They had told him before, but she saw that now he believed her. "She didn't want to see you again, she said — that's why my husband insisted that you weren't to write to her or to get in touch with her in any way."

"Do you think she'll — change her mind about that?" the boy asked, uncertainly, and Marion had to say she didn't know.

THEN, not looking at her, he said stiffly that he wanted to thank them for not letting his parents know. It wasn't that we were being considerate, Marion thought sadly, it was just that James didn't want anyone else to know.

"What about the baby?" the boy asked a little defiantly.

"It's been adopted, of course," Marion told him. "It — it was a boy."

He was silent for a long time, frowning, and then he asked what Diane had said about the baby. Marion looked at him, almost shocked.

"We don't speak about it at all," she told him. "Diane — I doubt if Di would even see it."

"You mean you don't know?" he asked her, and this time he was surprised. Then he stood up. "Mrs Martin, I'm going. You said Di would be home soon, so maybe it's better if I'm not around." His eyes met hers and held them. "Will you tell Mr Martin what I said — about wanting to see Diane? And when you think she'd see me, will you let me know? And — I'd like to know about the baby, what he was like . . ."

Marion nodded. "Why do you want to see Diane, Steve?"

"She's my girl," he returned roughly. "She's my girl, and just as soon as I can I'm going to marry her." He turned to go, but Marion put out her hand to stop him.

"Steve, it isn't just because you feel — guilty?" she asked hesitantly.

He looked down on her and the dark eyes were all at once years older and years wiser.

"Of course I feel guilty," he agreed. "I feel guilty as hell. About Di, about that little baby. But I love Diane and I'm not going to let her forget that."

DIANE was home right on time. Marion heard her walk up the garden path sedately and steadily, heard the front door close quietly behind her. She remembered the other days, when Diane's feet would come flying and the door would slam behind her, and she would be talking excitedly before Marion was even within sight.

"Sit down and have a cup of tea, Di — you didn't do any shopping?"

"I didn't need anything, Mum," Diane told her. "And I wanted to get home."

Marion sat down beside her and they talked politely about town, about the weather, about the play on TV later that night. And Marion kept thinking more and more of what Steve Ledgerwood had said just before he went away. Suddenly she put down her cup.

"Diane," she said, "I haven't asked you about the baby. Not because I didn't want to, but — I thought it was better . . ." Her voice tailed off, and she looked at her daughter, praying that she'd done the right thing.

"What do you want to know?" Diane asked at last, carefully.

Marion shook her head.

"Just — just tell me about him," she managed to whisper at last.

Diane was looking straight ahead of her.

"I only saw him a few times, you know," she said softly. "He was quite a big baby — eight pounds two ounces. They said he was a big baby, but — but he was very small in my arms. He was crying, and I took him and held him, and he was quiet. As if he knew that I was his mother." She was crying, silent tears running down her cheeks.

Marion stayed still, unwilling to move or speak in case Diane stopped.

"Funny, isn't it — such a little thing, and I only saw him a few times. I don't even remember giving birth to him, because they gave me something. Such a little thing," she said again slowly, wonderingly. "But — oh, Mummy, because of him, nothing will ever be the same again."

Marion was crying too as she held her daughter close. It was a long time before either of them spoke again.

"Why didn't you say that you wanted to keep him?" Marion asked. It was easy to say it, easy to speak to Diane now.

Diane shook her head. "It wasn't as easy as that, Mum. I — I knew it would be better all round for him to be adopted. We hadn't ever considered anything else. And — and when I held him it was the strangest thing. I wanted to keep him always, never to let him go, and yet at the same time I wanted him to have a proper home, with a mother and a father, and — and the sort of childhood a little boy should have." She was quiet for a long time, her face shadowed, remembering.

"No, I knew I shouldn't keep him, I knew it was best for him to be adopted, it was just — he was so little, and he fitted into my arms as if they were made for him."

She was silent again. So was Marion, thinking, with a surprisingly sharp sense of loss, of this little grandson whom she would never see. Her first grandchild.

"Who did he look like?" she asked then.

Diane smiled. "Red and angry, most of the time, and then he sneezed and just for a moment he looked ridiculously like Steve." ►p166

It's A Dog's Life

ME mam has always said it's rude to speak with your mouth full. As you can see, I'm the only polite one around here; these other two wouldn't look up from their noshing even if the roof fell in. At least, not until their dishes were licked clean.

Eating is something me mam taught us to take very seriously.

"Son," she used to say, "always remember there is nothing mor important than food. So learn to thin of your next meal, the one after that and the one after that!"

Me mam is very intelligent an does a lot of thinking. She's wonder fully well fed.

But take this lot here (please do 'cos I can't stand the sound of thei munching jaws) — they're as rud and savage as you'll find anywhere The sight and smell of food — an food — sends them stark ravin bonkers!

They rush at every meal as if it were

One Man's Meat . . . .

TO be fair, it is not often that the Man Of The House insists on playing his favourite records when we are entertaining guests. And frankly, I am very happy he doesn't insist very often.

After all, not everybody can stand the massed pipes and drums of the Scottish regiments playing "Scotland The Brave" . . . or the more deafening din of a jazz or rock band in full cry at an ear-shattering "session."

At the same time, I never try to stop him. If he wants to entertain our guests with his own particular choice of records, that is up to him — and them.

Except for one particular record! For that one particular record, I draw the line. To be more precise, I leave the room! I seize on the excuse of preparing a snack . . .

Now you might think that a rather unreasonable attitude for me to take. But I know, from long experience, that once this record is played, the Man Of The House gets launched into his wartime memories.

The songs remind him of this place and that, of this person and that, and before you can say "I surrender!" he's off . . . fighting the war over again.

Mind you, I notice that we British win the war a little harder, a little more by his own individual efforts, each time he retells his campaigns!

Bless him, he loves to live in the past! I don't mind one bit for myself. What I can't stand is the sheer enthusiasm in his eyes . . . and the yawn of his guests!

the last they were likely to get.

Me mam says we should share and share alike. And I think she's right. That's why I offer to share my bowl with the others, and expect to share theirs. Is it my fault I eat a little faster than them and my bowl is empty and theirs not?

I don't like old You-Know-Who making remarks about us when we're dining. He thinks he's such a scream when he comes in and says, "Is that thunder I'm hearing — oh no, I can see who's eating now!" Or "Listen to that crashing crescendo of crunching canines!"

Oh, he's funny. I don't think!

Besides, he's mean as well. The way he puts so *little* in each bowl, you'd think we were taking the very food out of his mouth. We would too, if only we could reach.

Yet you should see the amount of luvverly nosh he puts away! And with a great deal of slurp-lurp-swallow noises that any well-behaved dog would be ashamed of! He's so greedy he leaves nothing — not a tasty scrap — on his plate.

He's disgusting!

Oh well, I'm for off. Me mam gets fed about now. I'll go and faint from starvation just beside her. She's always good for an extra snack . . .

◀p163
And it was then, when Diane said his name, that Marion knew what she was going to do.

"Di," she said steadily, "Steve came to see you today."

All the colour left Diane's face.

"Why?" she whispered at last.

"He said that you're his girl, and he's going to marry you as soon as he can." Marion took both Diane's small hands in her own. "He said that he loves you, and he isn't going to let you forget it."

Diane had been looking down at her mother's hands covering hers. Now, when she looked up, her eyes were bright with tears. "I suppose you and Dad would think it's awful of me even to want to see him, after everything?"

Somehow or other, Marion thought, I'll make James understand. "You said at first that you didn't want him to marry you and you didn't want to see him again."

Diane shook her head.

"That's what I thought, then." Her voice wasn't quite steady. "There was plenty of time to think about it all, afterwards."

She looked up again, and her eyes held Marion's levelly. "This doesn't change anything, you know, Mum. Steve still has two years before he qualifies. We'd still have to — to wait." Just for a moment, her voice faltered over the word, then she went on, steadily.

"And that brings me to something I've been wanting to say. This secretarial course — I'm not right for it, Mum. I want to be a nurse." She smiled, but Marion could see the effort behind the smile. "It's not just because Steve's going to be a doctor, I really have often thought I'd like to do nursing. Only — you and Dad were so keen for me to go to university. What do you think Dad will say?"

"I don't know, Di," Marion replied slowly. "I don't know."

It was a shattering thought. All the years of their marriage, all the years of living together, all the good times and all the bad, and she didn't know what he would say. This whole thing, Marion thought unhappily, seems to have shaken the very roots of our marriage. I don't know how he'll take it.

THAT night, she told him everything. Sitting at the fire after Diane had gone to bed, she told him about Steve's visit and the things he'd said. And she told him everything that Diane had said and how she and Diane had wept together for the baby who was gone from them.

"Marion," he said at last, and his voice wasn't quite steady. "Come here, love."

She went into his arms and he held her close, neither of them saying anything. And even before he spoke, Marion knew it was going to be all right.

"You shouldn't have had all this on your own," he said eventually. "It isn't fair. I'm — sorry, Marion." He took a deep, steadying breath. "Right, what are we going to do about it all?"

"I don't think that's very hard to decide," Marion replied. His arm was around her shoulders, and for the first time in many months she felt that they were together.

"So Diane starts her nursing training, Steve goes on with his training, and at the end of it all they get married. If they still want to."

"If they still want to," Marion agreed. But she thought of the darkness in Steve's eyes and she thought of the way Diane had said his name.

"And — in the meantime?" James asked quietly. "For these two or three years?"

"We trust them," Marion said, her voice low.

After a moment he nodded.

"We trust them," he agreed levelly. "Right, Marion — tomorrow's Saturday, ring and ask him to come for lunch. Tell him Diane wants to see him and — I won't eat him."

It wasn't an easy meal. Steve was defensive, awkward, and Diane anxious and withdrawn. But when it was over Steve said he would help Diane with the dishes.

MARION and James waited. They talked in low voices. Tomorrow, Marion told him, they would go and see Margaret. It was a good idea, James agreed.

At last Steve and Diane came through and Diane said they were going for a walk. Marion stood at the window, watching them go down the garden path, and her heart ached as she remembered how it used to be when they went out, Diane's long hair flying, her small face raised eagerly to his, their hands touching. Now — they walked down the path carefully, not touching each other, not saying anything.

Unexpectedly, Diane turned and came back.

"We won't be long. Is it — is it all right, Mum?"

"Yes, Di, it's all right," Marion replied steadily. Then she turned away before Diane could see the tears stinging her eyes.

It would work out, she thought. Diane would do her nursing training, then in all probability she and Steve would marry. They'd have children, and they would have a good marriage, perhaps all the better for these waiting years.

And yet . . . Marion remembered her wedding day, and the look on James' face as she came to him in her white dress and her veil. She thought of the moment when he came to her after Margaret was born, and again after Diane was born, and the way he had touched each tiny crumpled face gently and wonderingly.

It couldn't ever be like that for Diane, for there would always be the memory of these last months.

"Marion, love," James said gently, putting his arm round her and drawing her towards him. "They'll be all right."

Marion looked again at the boy and the girl in the distance, and it seemed to her that they were a little closer now.

Steve would understand, she thought. The past months had changed him too. Though for both of them there would always be the thought of the baby, their son, growing up in someone else's house . . .

"Yes," she agreed. "They'll be all right."

But the tears were still in her eyes.

*** THE END ***

"Come To The Aid Of The Party"

Complete Story by
HONOR RORVIK

THAT'S all very well, Mr Goldwyn," Mother said to Clem, "but a camera will be cold comfort in your old age."

Mother was tireless in exhorting her eldest son to get married before it was too late. Her message was always the same, though she changed her form of address to match his current craze.

If it was engines he would be Mr Stephenson. If it was electricity his name was Edison. When he lectured her on the theory of musical composition she called him Sir Thomas, and on the frequent occasions when he advised her on how to run her home efficiently she would say, "Right-oh, Mr Beeton. I'll think about it."

Quite unruffled, Clem would grin amiably and retire into his one-man world.

Of course she adored him, but it didn't alter the fact that even I, the last of her brood, was married and awaiting my third child. Clem was showing touches of grey, but still far, far too much interest in machines.

"Machines earn me my bread and butter," was his constant protest.

"And your slice is big enough for two," was Mother's retort.

Clem would just smile easily and switch on his electric lathe.

He was interested in all sorts of things, was Clem, and so caught up in those interests that he was inclined to bore people. I'd often seen folk looking rather stunned when, in response to a mild show of curiosity, Clem treated them to a long lecture, laden with bewildering technical terms.

"Marriage would cure him of that," was my mother's fond belief. "You can't stand about delivering lectures when babies are hungry and housework must be done. Clem needs a wife. He needs someone to turn a deaf ear. I can't go on for ever."

She turned to me. "Surely you can do something, Liz. Have a dinner party and introduce him to a nice girl."

"To a nice deaf ear, you mean. Impossible, Mum." I shook my head. "I've introduced him to plenty. There was Janet. And Beth. And who could be nicer than Clare? Between you and me I think Clare had a little heartbreak over him."

"Hmm . . . " mused Mother. "Clem and Clare . . . Clare's that odd-eyed girl, isn't she?"

He was to be the magician and she, his beautiful assistant. Strange how, at the end of the day, she was the one who had worked all the magic . . .

"Odd-eyed! Really, Mum, what an awful description. She has one grey eye and one bluey-green eye. Her eyes drive most men mad with excitement, but Clem's never even noticed."

Then came my mother's birthday . . .

MY other brother, Christopher, brought his family down from the North, and my sister and her farmer husband managed to tear themselves away from their sheep and their porkers to join us for a family gathering.

Counting my two, there were nine grandchildren who were old enough to sit up for the celebration dinner.

"We'll get trestle tables, darling," my mother said. "We must book them early. And I'll have to raid you for chairs and spoons and things. We must ask Auntie Jean, and of course poor old Henry."

Poor old Henry was Mother's faithful admirer, but she was absolutely convinced that he and Auntie Jean would make a good, companionable couple.

I adore a get-together and tackled the project as enthusiastically as my mother. Both of us wanted to make it a memorable party.

"We must decorate the place from floor to ceiling," I decided. "I'll rope Clare in. She came to us for dinner at Christmas and we made some really fabulous decorations together."

"Darling, yes! What about asking her to join us?" Mum's eyes shone behind her glasses. "We could put her next to Clem and perhaps . . . "

"We'll put her next to poor old Henry and that will be a shot in the eye for you!"

"Well now, let's see," said my mother happily. "We must count heads. You'll do your special sauce, won't you, dear? And what about a punch bowl?"

"As long as you don't let Clem mix it," I said. "The last time he was let loose with the punch bowl everyone was reeling."

On the day of the party, Clare and I worked behind the closed doors of the play-room. We set four trestle tables in a square, with white cloths and scarlet napkins.

While we were clearing the last of Clem's bits and pieces out of the room, Clare pounced on a huge box full of miniature railway equipment.

"Look, Liz! The very thing."

In no time at all she had created a miniature enchantment running round the square of tables.

The train, its trucks laden with brightly-wrapped sweets for the children, moved at the touch of a switch — the one thing Clem was called on to organise — through a gay holiday countryside. There were clusters of tiny houses. Mirrors made lakes and ponds. There were swans, children playing, small figures waiting on the station platforms . And all around were flowers.

High above, in the centre of the square, hung a gigantic green-and-gold tinsel glove, and from it cascaded a score of streamers, each one reaching out to end in a bright wheel of colour in a wine-glass.

AS we were finishing, Mother poked her head round the door.

"Liz, dear," she said, obediently keeping her eyes shut, "don't you think we should get Merlin to entertain the children? They're getting wildly excited."

"Good idea, Mum. Ask him."

"Who's Merlin?" Clare said.

"Clem, of course. Magic is the latest craze. He's actually a member of the Magic Circle."

She said nothing.

I did a quick check on the placings. We hadn't put Clare next to poor old Henry after all. A Norwegian business associate of Christopher's had been invited to the party, and he was to sit beside Clare, with Christopher on the other side to make him feel at home.

We were standing back admiring our handiwork when there was a knock.

"You can't come in, whoever it is," I sang out forcefully.

"Come on out, Liz." It was Clem. "I need an accomplice because I want to show the folk my mind-reading trick."

"Nothing doing," I said. "I've done enough standing, and anyway, a magician's mate should never be in my delicate condition. Clare's here. What about her?"

"Don't be silly," Clare protested as we joined Clem in the hall. "I don't know the first thing about mind-reading."

"It's dead easy," I explained. "Clem blindfolds you and you stand in front of him with your back to the audience. Then people hold up objects and Clem either asks you who it is or what it is."

"And how do I work that lot out?"

"You put your hands on the sides of his face as if you're concentrating, and he rapidly clenches his teeth. You count the movements alphabetically. A, B, C, D, say, would give you D. Then he pauses and starts again and you count to H, and there you have the initials of Donald Harvey, my brother-in-law."

"But I don't know everybody's name."

"Well, if you don't know the name you put on a faraway voice and just give the initials. It makes it sound much more difficult. Clem will only ask for the object if it's a short word like pen or shoe. Come on. You'll do it beautifully."

Doubtfully, Clare agreed. "There's nothing but work around here," she said. "When do I get my taste of the punch, I'd like to know?"

"You can have a swig before we start," Clem comforted her. "I won't call for help right away."

The punch had been mixed by Christopher and Oscar, our Viking guest, and it was worth swigging. We all settled down, with the kids open-mouthed on the carpet, and witnessed the familiar routine of disappearing thimbles, diminishing balls, coloured handkerchiefs, and a top hat that produced things and lost them again.

Clare went bravely forward when Clem called for a volunteer and she quite outdid any performance of mine. She hesitated a second before she put her hands on the sides of his face and I wondered then if she had got over her private heartache.

I couldn't imagine Clem — or any other man, for that matter — not experiencing some sort of delicious reaction to her touch and to the closeness of so enchanting a creature.

Mother concluded the act by stealing up behind Clem and blindfolding him with her apron.

"Now tell the gathering what they will find in the play-room," she said, and Clem's answer, "Birthday dinner, folk!" was drowned by happy shouts.

IT was a terrific party. Christopher proposed the toast to Mother and I drank to her with a sentimental lump in my throat. Oscar sprang to his feet and said thank you to us all, lifting his glass to Mother and saying, *"Skaal!"* in the most delightful way.

His rugged Norse features and his polished manner made a devastating combination. In spite of Ian, my own hand-picked mate, I wished I were not so obviously pregnant. ►p174

Beware Of The CAT

EXCUSE me sniggering, but you people really are a funny lot!

To start with, you live all wrong. You work all day — when you should be resting. And you sleep all night — when you should be out enjoying yourselves.

You work hard to earn to buy expensive furniture, when all you really need is a cosy draught-free spot to lie down in, something soft to lay your head against, and some peace and quiet so that you can sleep undisturbed.

I don't understand all this must-go-to-work lark.

Having settled the question of one's comforts, there remains the question of one's food.

Now frankly I can't see you lot wriggling through the long grass around the compost heap in an effort to catch a field mouse or two. Neither can I imagine you hiding in a flower bed, making like a rose tree, until the right second to pounce on a bird silly enough to come within range.

So your food is quite a problem. If only you — but wait!

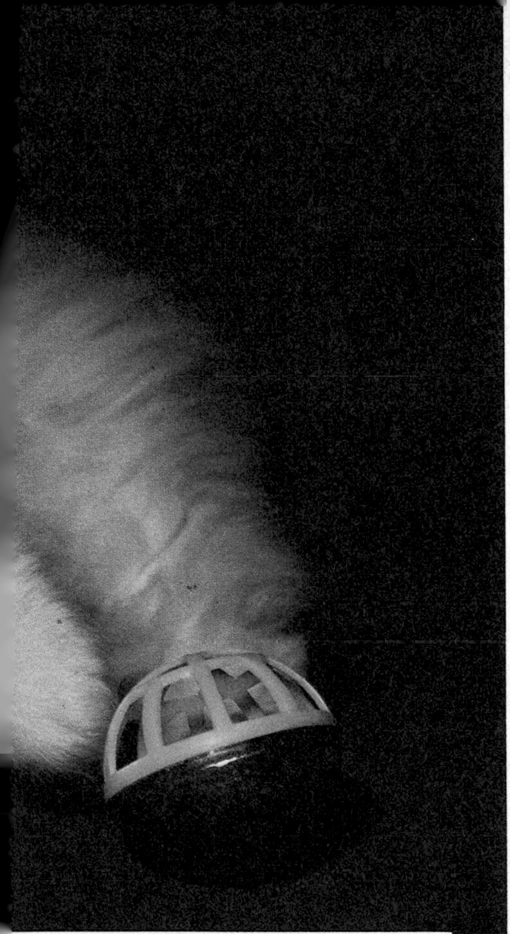

It strikes me that *my* food might well ecome more of a problem than it already s if you lot stopped buying liver and fish nd cans of lovely food.

Which means of course I've been rather asty in suggesting you change your way f life at all.

Indeed, on reflection I am more than onvinced that you wonderful lot are really oing a grand job, earning all that lovely olly with which to buy poor deserving ases like myself more lovely nosh.

So press on — regardless. Regardless f anything you might hear or say or learn o the contrary.

And by the way, if you should happen to e working a little harder and longer and ore profitably just now, I would mention hat I haven't tasted a rainbow trout or a cotch salmon in ages . . .

A Little Too Impulsive!

IT was her very first visit to an auction sale and, as my young friend confessed later, she got carried away with the excitement!

She had gone to the sale because she wanted to buy a good second-hand cabin trunk — and there was a choice of four advertised in the sale.

She got her cabin trunk, just the size she wanted and in good condition, at a ridiculously low figure. And that was the start of the trouble.

Having paid so little, she began to be "bargain-conscious." She began to bid for all sorts of things . . . because they were going so cheaply.

And, as often happens at small sales, she got a few.

Deckchairs at throwaway prices . . . a reading lamp for a few pence . . . a bedroom clock almost for nothing . . . four dozen plant pots varying in size from the very smallest to the largest . . . an old-fashioned but beautifully inlaid occasional table (which has one leg needing a little attention).

She arrived home flushed with success. And only then did she remember that her family have all the deck-chairs they need, all the reading lamps necessary, an electric alarm clock in every bedroom, and no space in any room for an extra occasional table.

But at least her father was happy to take the plant pots for his already well-stocked greenhouse!

Her first auction sale . . . and her last!

◀p171

I noticed Oscar saying, *"Skaal!"* to Clare and holding her eyes with his over the rim of his glass. Snatching a glance at Clem, I saw that he had not missed this little trick.

As she had been blindfolded during the magician's act I suppose that Clem was still unaware of the special quality of Clare's eyes.

Oscar was finding it hard to look anywhere but at her enchanting face.

Mother's newly-set hair had sprung back into its gay curls and her cheeks were sweetly pink.

After dinner Oscar and Clare were divided by Christopher, who drew his associate aside for business talk.

Auntie Jean nodded off and poor old Henry furtively stole away to sit beside Mother.

"More coffee, Henry? Oh, it's empty. We'll have to get some more made. Liz, dear, are you too exhausted?"

To tell the truth I was dead beat. Clare, who had been talking to my Ian, held out her hand for the pot.

"Let me, Mrs Dennis. I'd love to." She smiled at Ian and went out of the room with that devastating walk of hers.

Ian creaked his long frame on to a cushion beside me.

"She's nice," he said.

I nodded.

"How are you doing, Liz?" he said, reaching for my hand. "We don't seem to have seen each other since the punch."

"I'm fine. It was a good party, wasn't it?"

"Great, I bet some of the kids could do with a dose of magnesia."

"Me too." I patted my tummy. "But it was worth it."

Most of us felt the same way, judging by the desultory talk. Only Christopher and Oscar kept up a serious-sounding rumble on the other side of the room.

I pulled myself together. If I didn't stir my lazy bones and do something I might easily drop off too.

I patted Ian's hand and rose.

"I'll just go and give Clare a hand," I said. "You talk to Clem or someone . . ."

BUT Clem was not there to talk to. He was in the kitchen with Clare. I nearly walked in on them, but Clem and his accomplice didn't hear me.

They were sitting on opposite sides of the kitchen table, holding hands, the coffee-pot cold and forgotten. Clare's eyes were shut and my brother was gazing at her, fascinated.

Slowly she opened one eye.

"Green," Clem said.

She closed the green eye and opened the other one.

"Grey," said Clem.

Fixing him with her grey eye, Clare said, "It's magic, you see."

And Clem leant towards her across the table murmuring, "Real magic . . ."

I tiptoed away, and as I went I heard Clare say, "But there's just one thing. I refuse to dress up in pink tights and be cut in half . . ."

*** THE END ***